Poor Smokers

Alan Marsh and Stephen McKay

Policy Studies Institute

012998

POLICY STUDIES INSTITUTE
100 Park Village East, London NW1 3SR

ISBN 0 85374 589 7

PSI Research Report 771

A CIP catalogue record for this book is available from the British Library.

1 2 3 4 5 6 7 8 9

PSI publications are available from
BEBC Distribution Ltd
PO BOx 1496, Poole, Dorset, BH12 3YD

Books will normally be despatched within 24 hours. Cheques should be made payable to BEBC Distribution Ltd

Credit card and telephone/fax orders may be placed on the following freephone numbers:

FREEPHONE: 0800 262260
FREEFAX 0800 262266

Booktrade Representation:
Broadcast Books, 24 De Montfort Road, London SW16 1LW

PSI subscriptions are available from PSI's subscription agent
Carfax Publishing Company Ltd
PO Box 25, Abingdon, Oxford OX14 3UE

Laserset by Stanford DTP, Milton Keynes, Bucks MK17 9JP
Printed in Great Britain by Bourne Press, Bournemouth, BH1 4QA

Acknowledgements

The data used in this study were collected for a major programme of research into Britain's low income families. This work was carried out by the Social Security Research Team in the Policy Studies Institute's Family Finances Group for the Department of Social Security. We are grateful for the Department's permission to use the data for this analysis of the effects of smoking.

The work for this report was carried out for the Health Education Authority who supported this part of the study.

At HEA, Patti White and her colleagues gave us much help and encouragement.

We are grateful for the help and advice of Hilary Graham. We also owe special thanks both to Eileen Goddard at the Social Survey Division of the Office of Population Censuses and Surveys and to Martin Jarvis at the National Addiction Centre who carried out for us a special analysis of the General Household Survey.

In June 1993, a draft of this report was read and discussed by a group of 25 people from the fields of health education, social policy research and government departments. Their comment and advice was invaluable.

Alan Marsh and Stephen McKay
Policy Studies Institute

January 1994

Contents

1   What Is The Problem?

Introduction

It is official policy to discourage people from smoking, and to help them avoid the increased risks of lung cancer, heart disease and other illness that smoking causes. Part of this policy is to increase the excise duty on tobacco products each year. This maintains or increases the real cost of smoking to a level most people will find at least noticeable and gives smokers an additional incentive to give up.

The problem is that this policy is having no effect at all on those least able to afford to buy cigarettes: Britain's low income families. They do not give up smoking in response to price rises. The only effect such price rises have is to increase the hardship experienced by poor smokers, for them and for their children.

This report examines the extent of this problem and its effects. The study addresses a major policy dilemma in smoking control: tobacco taxation is a benefit to the majority because it reduces cigarette consumption. Some smokers themselves say they welcome it (Marsh and Matheson, 1983). But it is doing harm among a minority – among the poorest families who find it too difficult to give up smoking however much it costs. Tobacco tax has become the most regressive tax we have. It is a familiar dilemma, but one that has intensified over the past 15 years. During this time, three trends have combined:

- Smoking has become increasingly concentrated among poor people, especially among poor women.
- There have been considerable increases in income inequalities in general, and especially among families with dependent children.
- More recently tobacco tax increases have raised the real price of cigarettes consistently ahead of price inflation. Further such increases are promised.

These trends have greatly intensified both the regressive nature of tobacco taxation and its likely effects on the welfare of low income families who smoke.

We know very little of the processes that have caused the social division of smoking to become so marked among the lowest income groups. We know almost nothing about the impact of smoking upon the material well-being of low income families. This lack of data, was described by the ASH report, *Her Share of Misfortune,* as:

> ... a spectacular and inexcusable lack of research into the relationship between social disadvantage and cigarette smoking, in general, and particularly among women. (p.5)

The social distribution of smoking

The social distribution of smoking has changed to the extent that a new view may have to be taken of its social origins and its control.

In the population as a whole, the prevalence of smoking has fallen. Among men, prevalence has declined steadily since the late 1940's when nearly eight out of ten men smoked, down to present levels of just over 28 per cent . (General Household Survey, OPCS, 1994). Among women, smoking prevalence rose to its highest levels of just over 40 per cent in the 1960s and subsequently declined to less than 30 per cent, consistently a percentage point or two below the annual prevalence rates reported for men. (See Figure 1.1)

In successively younger age cohorts below 50, the prevalence of smoking among men and women is increasingly similar. Among the youngest, it is more or less the same. Among some younger sub groups, women show a slightly higher prevalence of smoking than men's.

While the sexual division of smoking has narrowed almost to parity, the social class division has widened. Professional groups have always had a comparatively low prevalence of smoking, men and women alike, falling in unison from a third in 1972 to 14 per cent in 1992. Among non-manual groups as a whole, a narrow sex difference in smoking prevalence had all but disappeared by 1980 (33 per cent for men, 32 per cent for women) and the two rates also fell to 22 per cent and 23 per cent respectively by 1992.

In contrast, people in the manual working class groups always had much higher rates of smoking in the past and so their reduction in smoking prevalence seems equally impressive. Among skilled and semi-

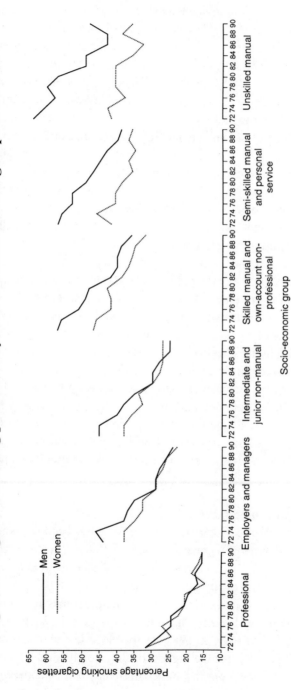

Figure 1.1 Cigarette Smoking prevalence by sex and socio-economic group: 1972–1990

Source: 1990 Smoking monitor, OPCS, SS 91/3, HMSO, 26 November 1991

skilled men, for example, prevalence has declined from 57 per cent to 36 per cent in 20 years (1972-92). Since half of all men inhabit this socio economic group, it is they who have provided the greatest aggregate decline in smoking. The steepest decline in the same 16 years is seen in the smaller group of unskilled manual SEG: 68 per cent of whom were still smoking as late as 1972; down to 42 per cent in 1992. These figures are for cigarette smoking so some of this decline is due to men (and not women) switching to pipes and cigars. Some of it is also due, especially in the unskilled group, to the differential mortality that smoking causes – there are two ways to become an ex-smoker.

So it is important to bear in mind that the social class difference in smoking prevalence seen in the present figures are due to different rates of smoking recruitment and cessation between them, and even these conceal some important within-class differences.

Thus, among men, the middle class smoke least; the majority of ex-smokers are skilled workers; the unskilled appear to have come furthest away from smoking but they still have much the furthest to go.

Among women, the middle class also smoke least (though there is evidence of a cadre of smokers among private sector female managers); but only shallow falls are seen in the prevalence figures for working class women up to 1984 and little change since then.

These trends have increasingly associated smoking with social and income inequalities. There are signs that smoking will be increasingly associated with sexual inequalities too, especially among families. The reason for this is that family poverty itself has grown and has become increasingly associated with women's poverty. We examine this point next.

Changes in income inequalities.
During the time that the distribution of smoking has become increasingly concentrated into low income groups, the difference in real incomes between the low and higher income strata has widened considerably. As Figure 1.2 shows, most of the growth in incomes in the past 15 years has gone to those on or above average earnings. Real incomes in the lowest decile of the income distribution have increased by only 2 per cent in 15 years; compared to over 20 per cent for those just above average earnings and 57 per cent for the highest decile. Nearly all the increase in standards of living have gone to families above the fourth income decile.

Figure 1.2 Percent increase in income 1979–1990

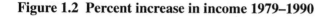

per cent increase in net income

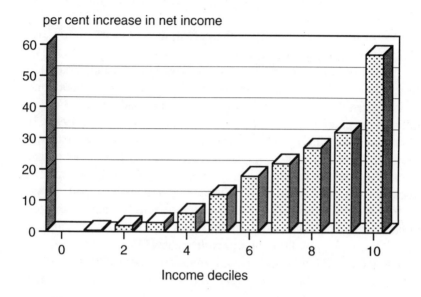

Income deciles

Thus smoking is becoming concentrated among the relatively poor who, at the same time, are becoming relatively poorer.

Both of these trends are occurring at an accelerating rate, especially during this recent time of recession and high unemployment. During the same period of time, unemployment has increased fourfold and become endemic among the least skilled. The income instability and the uncertainty and anxieties that go with unemployment and the threat of unemployment, have become the common experience of the majority of lower income earners. The numbers receiving means tested benefits have doubled, despite their withdrawal from significant groups such as unemployed young people and students.

These widening income inequalities have been most significant among families. The proportion of children living in families drawing means tested benefits has doubled from one sixth to a third. Recently too there has been a sharp growth in problem debts that is concentrated in poor families, especially those with two or more children (Berthoud and Kempson, 1992). There are, in absolute terms, more poor families whose incomes contrast more sharply than before with the incomes – and of course with the housing and material welfare – of better off

5

families. As the ASH women and smoking study group pointed out in their report 'Her Share of Misfortune', where there is family poverty, there is women's poverty and usually more of it.

One of the reasons for this is that, often, incomes are unfairly distributed in two adult families in favour of mens' consumption (Pahl, 1984). The greater reason of course is the rapid growth in the numbers of lone parent families (Glendinning and Millar 1988). In 1971, 570,000 lone parents cared for a million children. In 1991 they had increased to 1.3 million lone parents caring for two million children (Haskey, 1993). If these trends have continued, there are now 1.4 million or more than one in six of all families headed by one parent, usually a woman. About two thirds of lone parent families receive income support and between them make up 7 out of 10 of all families who live on income support.

It was known that women in low income families have the more intractably high prevalence of smoking. Looking carefully at Figure 1.1, it is very striking how little their prevalence has fallen since 1984, and some hint that it might be rising again against the national trend. Again, the rise in lone parenthood may very well underlie this. There has been evidence for some while (Marsh and Matheson, 1983) that lone mothers have an uncommonly high prevalence of smoking. When they were few it was 'less of a problem'. Now they are many, and they are becoming a more and more significant group among smokers as the smoking population shrinks around them.

There may also be special problems among couples. Women in low income couples very often share their smoking habits with their partners. Those who do, together with the lone parents, are now right at the centre of the smoking problem as a whole and together they give every impression of having been put there, or at least kept there, by income inequality.

There is much that is unknown about this dual process. It may be that it is the correlates of income inequality, and moreover *changes* in these correlates, that are important. For example, working class families who have moved up the income distribution have signalled this change in station by buying their homes. Over a million have bought their council homes. Those that could not, the unemployed, lone parents, and so on, remained in the hard-to-let and harder-to-sell estates and flats. The social profile of social tenants has changed in the past 15 years. The proportion of social tenant households headed by a woman has risen from 31 per cent to 41 per cent between 1981 and 1988/9 (OPCS, 1991). Lone parents are 4 per cent of all households but 14 per cent of social tenants. Many of the rest are families headed by unemployed or casually employed unskilled men. The proportion of economically inactive social tenants has risen from 42 per cent to 60 per cent in seven years. What used to be the continuous thread of shared working class life of semi-skilled and unskilled workers-in-work, has been broken up into small groups of dis-possessed people who are competing for a diminishing social wage.

These trends have intensified the geographical and social isolation of low income families from mainstream life. Lately, it is people in the mainstream of life that have been giving up smoking. Whatever has been causing this – and it is not completely certain what has been causing it – low income groups have been more and more effectively divided from it. It has been suggested that smoking has become for many poor people a perverse celebration of 'underclass' status. Certainly many lone parents say, often with some force, that smoking is their only luxury (Graham, 1989). When many luxuries appear the normal entitlement of others, one luxury may be a necessity. If it is also the one that provides the sole anodyne for family life on benefit incomes, it is likely to be defended.

Changes in policy.

Successive governments have supported a smoking control policy that has several elements:

- a varied programme of health education discouraging smoking and supporting research
- support for campaigning and intervention agencies such as Action on Smoking and Health
- training for health professionals for anti-smoking intervention
- maintaining a voluntary agreement with tobacco manufacturers to restrict advertising in scope and volume and carry health warnings of increasing variety and directness
- banning sales to children and increasing the penalties for offenders
- maintaining and then increasing the real price of tobacco products through rises in taxation and changes in the tobacco tax structure.
- manipulating the tax levels in favour of lower tar brands and moving towards a change in the tax structure that will make the cheapest cigarettes rise faster in price than they would previously have done.

Governments have an interest in tobacco price maintenance through taxation that is not connected to health policy; it is a major source of revenue. But by the 1970s, cigarettes had become less expensive relative to overall inflation and especially to wage inflation. This post war period also saw a rise in both prevalence and consumption, though again it should be remembered that much of this rise was the late entry of women into the higher prevalence figures and their startling increase in consumption: from 71 cigarettes per female smoker per week in 1956 to over 120 throughout the 1970s. Men's consumption rose less in the same period (121 to 150 per smoker) while their prevalence figures fell significantly (see Wald, et al, 1990)

Subsequent falls among non-manual groups in the 1970s were attributed, probably rightly, to the success of health education and to shifts in middle class ideas of self-presentation and personal efficacy that have continued since. Townsend (1988) attributes the class divergence in smoking prevalence that emerged in the 1970s to a response by the educated non-manual groups to health education during a time when lower income, less educated smokers meanwhile were 'benefiting' from relative price reductions. Only when the Callaghan budget of 1977 advanced tobacco tax beyond inflation and, following two further falls, the first Howe budget of 1980 started a steady increase in real price, did the new decline in smoking set in among manual working class groups.

This evidence, and similar evidence from Europe and America suggests that there is a reliable inverse relationship between real price of cigarettes and consumption. Therefore both the price elasticity of tobacco products is favourable to the use of price increases beyond inflation to reduce consumption further. Townsend and others have estimated that each 1 per cent increase in real price yields a 0.5 per cent decrease in consumption. (cf. Godfrey, 1989, who cites a range of UK and international evidence indicating this order of price elasticity). Whereas these considerations do not much trouble the well off, they bear more heavily upon those with little disposable income, who ought then to reconsider the usefulness of their smoking.

On the evidence of recent budgets, there has been a shift in policy towards price increase as the main part of policy towards smoking. This may be in part a compensatory move that defends the decision not to expand other elements of smoking control policy. For example, the government has consistently stood out against a ban on tobacco advertising and promotion on grounds of the defence of liberty to advertise a legal product and the comparative efficacy of other methods. Tax increases have also been encouraged by the view that a tobacco tax policy that lags behind inflation will actually decrease total revenues compared with one that moves a little ahead.

The key argument supporting this policy is that while tobacco taxation is clearly regressive, and increasingly so, *changes* in tax levels are not regressive because those with lowest incomes, it is believed, are most likely to reduce their consumption of tobacco in the face of real price increases. Since it is they who smoke most, and for other reasons suffer the poorest health, this is an especially desirable goal.

Why are these changes important?

No real issue is taken here with these arguments about either the price or income elasticities of demand for tobacco, save to say that the relationship between price and prevalence is a lot more complicated and uncertain than that between price and consumption. Nor do we wish to join in the arguments about the extent to which variation in price through taxation may be regressive at the margins. Our point is that for those who do not reduce their consumption in response to tax increases, the policy is highly regressive. The reason is that the people who are not responding to tax increases by giving up smoking are the poor, and the poorest smokers. Evidence for this is given in Chapter 3.

This would be less of a problem if everyone affected by the cost of smoking were free-choosing individuals. The problem becomes more significant in the case of low income families who nowadays make up nearly all of the *working* poor and the majority of the non-working poor under pensionable age. They have dependents: among low income families, couples usually have one non-working partner, and they have children.

A low income couple with two children, for example, in work and receiving child benefit and an average amount of family credit (provided they claim it), will nowadays typically have an income of about £160 a week. They will not receive housing benefit or community charge benefit. If both smoke 20 cigarettes a day, and we shall show this is not at all uncommon, their weekly expenditure on tobacco will be about £22. If they have fixed costs of, typically, £80 a week, then tobacco accounts for about a quarter of their disposable income. This clearly has implications for their ability to meet weekly budgeting items for food, clothing and similar basics. If they continue to smoke, real increases in tobacco price will result in real decreases in expenditure on essential items. This is likely to include expenditure that impinges on the welfare of children. This is the evidence of Chapter 4.

We accept entirely that the welfare of children in such families is better served by the abandonment of smoking in their homes, both in terms of their health, as less well-nourished secondary smokers, and in the better provision of family living standards that should result. But the problem remains that most such families are likely to continue to smoke even in the face of the highest tax increases thought politically tolerable. It creates a hard policy choice whose mechanisms – what is affecting what and by how much – are very poorly understood.

What is to be done?
The account of research that follows addresses this hard policy choice, by:

- describing the new contours of social and economic disadvantage among Britain's low income families
- establishing in detail the prevalence of smoking and the consumption of cigarettes among Britain's low income families,
- establishing what kinds of low income families smoke, smoke most, or not at all
- considering the causes of smoking among low income families
- examining the impact of smoking on family living standards
- examining the likely effects of further real increases in tobacco taxation on both the prevalence of smoking and the welfare of families.

First, in the following chapter, we establish who are Britain's low income families and describe the details of their circumstances, and how they differ from one another and from better off families.

2 Who Are Britain's Low Income Families?

Introduction

Most of the evidence examined in this study is drawn from the Programme of Research Into Low Income Families (PRILIF) being carried out at PSI on behalf of the Department of Social Security. The first report, *Families, Work and Benefits* (Marsh and McKay 1993) looked at the effects of social security benefits on families in and out of work. For this study, an important aspect of the earlier work was the development of a unified description of family poverty. We showed how social tenancy, experience of means-tested benefits, lack of educational qualifications, unemployment, and manual work were all markers for disadvantage. These markers combined to increase families' risk of being in severe hardship by several orders of magnitude, additionally to the effects of family income. This was true for couples as well as for lone parents. So powerful were these effects that they create a deep 'fault line' in the social geography of low income families, dividing them from other more advantaged families.

The study

In 1991, the Policy Studies Institute carried out on behalf of the Department of Social Security a survey of 2,200 low income families. The main purpose was to study the effects of benefits upon work and well-being among families with dependent children. There was strong interest in the effects of 'in-work' benefits, especially the effect of family credit. Nearly all parents of dependent children get child benefit and, where appropriate, one parent benefit. Anyone in low paid work may claim some means tested benefits such as housing benefit and help, then, with their community charge. Family credit is also means tested, but only *working families* may claim it. Seven families in every hundred receive family credit nowadays and they get an average of about £42 a week.

Thus, among working families, eligibility for family credit is the most important marker for low income *relative to the size of the family.* Family credit is a cash benefit, with some associated welfare provisions, that may be claimed by parents who work more than 15 hours a week (though at the time of the survey, in 1991, the weekly qualifying hours were 24), whose children are of dependent age and whose net family income falls below a specified level. This threshold level is determined by the numbers and ages of the children in the family and is compared to the family's total income. The amounts paid are linked to the amounts of income support and associated benefits that would be paid if the parents were not in full-time work.

For this reason, it is possible to define low income families as families who are within range of the qualifying provisions of family credit – including those who *might* claim the benefit if their circumstances changed, as well as those who actually received it. These potential claimants may be either seeking or entering low-paid work, working and eligible to claim, or have incomes just beyond the scope of the benefit. It was an important aspect of the study to find among those families who were working and, though eligible for family credit, had nonetheless failed to claim it. These are referred to as eligible non-claimants (ENCs).
In this way, we defined low income families as:

> families whose total income from all sources was less than 25 per cent *above* the most they could receive before their entitlement to family credit expires.

It is important to note that this definition of 'a low income family' depends on the numbers of children in the family and their ages. Thus a couple with one four year child earning £162.50 a week net would not be selected. A couple with four children over 12 earning £180 a week net would be selected. The definition includes the bottom 25 per cent of the *equivalent* income distribution among families.

However, the focus of the content of the study also meant that we needed to talk to unequal numbers of these four groups. We needed a lot of family credit claimants, for example, but rather fewer higher income or out of work families.

The real problem was that low income families, *in the population as a whole*, are not common. Our total sample population was hidden away in only 12 per cent of all addresses. This is an unpromising prospect for a general population sift to find those wanted for interview. This is shown in Figure 2.1

Figure 2.1 The location of the four 'target groups' in the relative income distribution among families

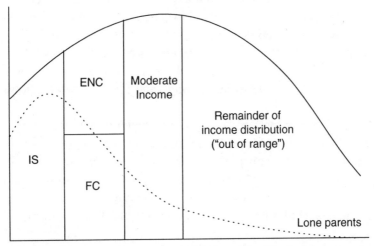

ENC = eligible non-claimants   FC = family credit   IS = income support

The solutions found to the sampling problems are described in detail in the main report (Marsh and McKay, 1993). In brief, it was decided to carry out a postal sift of families included on the child benefit record system in the DSS computer in Washington, Tyne & Wear. This sift would take the form of a postal self completion questionnaire that would identify low income families among those who replied. 14,400 families were sampled and each sent a postal questionnaire asking about work, income, and receipt of benefit or maintenance. 9700 families replied.

In addition, the DSS family credit record in North Fylde was programmed to select in each of the same postal areas used for the child benefit sample, twice the number of family credit recipients discovered by the sift.

The interviews with selected low income families were carried out by NOP. Interviews were obtained from 82 per cent of those approached, though 7 per cent were interviews where only one partner in a couple had been personally interviewed and the partner data, where possible, completed by proxy.

Work and earnings

It is worth looking in detail at the patterns of work and earnings that distinguish low income families from the rest. Social security benefits apart, what is low income? What do low paid families earn?

The details are given in Table 2.1, which show, separately for low income and higher income families the proportions or men and working full time or part time (adopting the 1991 family credit rules of 24 hours a week or more) and their median earnings, and Table 2.2, which shows earnings in greater detail.

Being a low income family is largely a matter of having no job or low pay, often low female pay. Being a higher income family is largely a matter of being a two earner family or having high male wages, or both.

Among lone parents, almost all the higher income group work full time, and a quarter of them are men. Among the low income group, only 19 per cent work full time and 11 per cent part time. They are nearly all women.

Among couples, the pattern is naturally more complicated. Nearly all the higher income men have full time jobs, of course, and the majority of these have working wives too: only 3 in 10 higher income couples rely solely on male earnings, almost none on sole female earnings. In contrast, only 15 per cent of low income couples have two jobs, 40 per cent have sole male earnings, and, again unlike higher income couples, 10 per cent have sole female earnings, though half only part time. A third of low income families have no work at all.

Among main wage earners – lone parents and husbands – the earnings distributions comparing low income with higher income families scarcely overlap. Among low income families, take home pay is typically less than £200 a week; among higher income families, £200 is almost universally a minimum take home wage. Higher income families do not merely earn more, they earn twice as much as low income families. For example, among lone parents working full time the median earnings of low income families are £105 a week, among higher income families, £207 a week in take home pay. Among full time working husbands, the gap is widest: £150 a week among low income husbands, £378 a week among higher income husbands.

Table 2.1 Patterns of work and median net weekly earnings among low income and higher income families with dependent children.

	Low income		Higher income	
Lone parents (n=2007)	%	Median earnings (£s p.w.)	%	Median earnings (£s p.w.)
Working 24 hrs a week+:	19	105	95	207
Working less than 24 hrs	} 31%		} 97%	
a week	12	28	2	–
Not working	69	–	3	–
	100		100	
Married women (n=6218)	%	Median earnings (£s p.w.)	%	Median earnings (£s p.w.)
Working full-time	9	82	37	134
	} 26%		} 71%	
Working part-time	17	39	34	67
Not working	74	–	29	–
Married men (n=6218)				
Working full-time	54	150	97	293
	} 55%		} 98%	
Working part-time	1	(56)	*	(247)
Not Working	44	–	2	–
Couples with children (n=6218)	%	Median earnings (£s p.w.)	%	Median earnings (£s p.w.)
Both work, >24hrs	4	171	36	340
He works, she works part-time	11	169	34	278
He works, she does not	40	140	29	260
She works full-time, he does not	5	97	1	224
She works part-time, he does not	5	40	*	–
Neither work	33	–	*	–
All	100	139	100	292

Table 2.2 The earnings of low income and higher income families

	Low income			Higher income		
	Lone parents	Married women	Married men	Lone parents	Married women	Married men
Take home pay in £s per week						
	%	%	%	%	%	%
1–50	34	53	3	0	24	0
50–100	32	35	12	3	35	0
100–150	28	10	38	8	20	0
150–200	5	1	42	36	0	10
200–250	1	*	4	30	7	22
250–300	0	0	*	15	3	22
Over 300	0	0	0	8	3	46
	100%					
Average earnings	79	57	144	228	114	378
Median earnings	77	49	150	206	88	293
Average pay, (£s per hour)	3.10	2.9	3.2	6.1	4.5	7.0
Median pay, (£s per hour)	3.00	2.9	3.3	5.4	3.6	5.4

The composition of low income families

Having identified our sample of low income families, the next step was to divide them into the four target groups that formed the basic design – or rather eight groups since we would want to look at lone parents and couples separately.

These are actual numbers interviewed:

Table 2.3 Target groups interviewed

	Eligible non-claimants	Family credit claimants families	Moderate income families	Out of full-time work
Lone Parents	57	322	72	432
Couples	157	496	416	239

When the numbers above are re-weighted to reflect their true position, relative to one another, this is how the eight groups appear in the population *of low income families.*

Table 2.4 Relative size of target groups
Percentages of total weighted sample

	Eligible non-claimants	Family credit claimants families	Moderate income families	Out of full-time work
Lone parents	2%	5%	3%	38%
Couples	6%	8%	20%	18%
ALL	8%	13%	23%	56%

The pre-eminence of out of work lone parents as a presence among low income families is very striking: nearly 4 out of 10 of them. Together with the minority who had jobs, lone parents make up nearly half of all low income families. Nearly all of those we have called the moderate income group (families between 1 per cent and 25 per cent above their FC threshold) are couples.

In summary: 1 in 10 of the couples had yet to marry (Table 2.5). Most of the lone parents were formerly married, though more of the out of work lone parents were single. Lone parents had fewer children than couples and the point made earlier about working lone parents having older children is seen very clearly. Black people, of all kinds, are about 4 per cent of the British population but are 10 per cent of low income families.

Among couples in low income families, it is usually the male partner who has a paid job, if either of them have a job, though about one in seven of the working couples have two earners and one in ten of the out of work couples have some part time work.

If the Standard Classification of Occupations is used to code the jobs reported by low income families, most of them end up in just a few categories of often unskilled work. This is made worse by the large numbers of women to be coded. In fact, the majority of jobs to be coded were women's jobs. Low paid female workers are almost invisible to the SCO. Using the data, a new occupational scale was created for low income jobs. It discriminates between 20 low paid occupations.

The women tend to be found in junior non manual grades, selling and personal service jobs, or they are cooks and cleaners. In fact the majority of low paid women do one of five jobs that all begin with 'C': cooks, cleaners, cashiers, childminders and clerks. The men are found more often in the less skilled manual grades in production, construction and food industries; others are drivers and warehousemen.

Table 2.5 A social profile of low income families

Cell percentages

	'Benefit families'				*'Non-benefit families'*			
	Lone parents		Couples		Lone parents		Couples	
	Out of work	FC clmts	Out of work	FC clmts	Eligible non-clmts	Mod. income	Eligible non-clmts	Mod income
% legally married			85	83			91	93
% never married	49	43			31	19		
% 3+ children	22	18	36	48	16	7	40	30
% yougest 0–4	52	21	52	54	21	13	53	51
% non-white	9	6	10	15	18	12	18	7
% social tenants	65	52	61	52	27	18	29	27
% no qualifications (f)	46	47	56	52	29	11	39	42
(m)			58	51			45	37
% manual workers	53	34	83	78	18	17	63	64
Total weekly disposable income (£)	82	148	111	162	138	203	126	259

Low income families in and out of work: a summary

Apart from their low incomes, low income families are different from other families in a number of key aspects:

- The lowest income strata 'capture' most of the lone parent families; nine out of ten of them. Nearly *half* of our sample of low income families were lone parents. Two thirds of these lived on income support, sometimes doing a little part time work. They remained on income support for a long while, typically twice as long as IS claimant couples. The barriers they faced entering work were familiar but intractable: little education, training or work experience; a lack of really suitable jobs; uncertain childcare; a lack of regular maintenance payments; and a loss of all income support on earnings above £15 a week that debarred lone parents from a gradual increase in working hours as their children grow older. To get into work, they needed full time hours or very few.

- But lone parents are not low income families just because they are lone parents. Most of them are women, so the one third of lone parents who get paid jobs tend to be offered lower wages. A quarter of low income lone parents work full time and nearly four out of ten of these in full time work have incomes low enough to qualify for family credit (compared with 5 per cent of all couples and 16 per cent of low income couples), even though they have fewer children than couples have.

- Couples, on the other hand, are found among low income families when only one of them works full time, when the main earners' wages are low (though not necessarily the lowest, by any means) and when the children are young. A couple's route out of low income is to become a two earner family.

- However, women in low income couples face similar disincentives to work that conspire to keep lone parents at home: similarly low levels of education, training and really suitable jobs. They too are offered wages that would pay for little childcare if they needed too; usually they don't. If it does, they will soon find going out to work becomes economically irrational. They have an advantage in being able to ease themselves into work more gradually, increasing their hours as children grow. But if they are on family credit this advantage vanishes. The wives in family credit couples have the same problems as lone parents on IS. True they lose 'only' 70 per cent of family credit (though more if they are on HB & CCB too) for each pound they earn, but they get no £15 a week disregard as those on IS do. The fixed 6 month term of FC awards cushions this disincentive a little, but nearly all of the 1 in 6 low income couples getting family credit were one earner families – though some of them are women full time workers.

- A surprising number – 1 in 6 of working low income families – were self employed.

- Thirty years ago, when families had two parents and one job, a survey of low income families would have placed unskilled manual work at the fore of any social construction of their position. No longer – the growth of out of work lone parenthood, and higher unemployment generally has changed it. A fifth of lone parents who work had the poorest jobs in cleaning and catering, the rest worked in junior non manual, retail and personal service jobs. The same is true of wives and even of their husbands, still less than half of whom are manual workers. Our definition of low income includes many moderately paid non-manually employed families, especially if they have more than two children. But the emphasis has shifted from work to benefits: 59 per cent of low income families claimed means tested benefits; another 8 per cent were entitled to them but did not claim; 33 per cent had only earnings and non means tested benefits.

- The gap in earning power 'caused' by having children occurs at the point of greatest family needs. It happens as families move through a quite narrow band of time in their life cycle as they bring up young children. Thus, the central definition of low income – eligibility for familiy credit – tends to include lone parents whose children are old enough to look after themselves, and for couples whose children are not.

The 'benefit fault line'

The characteristics of low income families described above are not shared uniformly. Low income families are not all alike. We argue that there is a kind of geological fault line that runs through the population of low income families. It places the two 'benefit families' (those in work and claiming FC, or out of work and claiming IS) on one side and the two non benefit families (eligible non claimants of FC and the moderate income families) on the other.

The benefit families, compared to the others, tend of course to be lone parents. Among lone parents, they tend to be single or separated from a cohabitation, rather than formerly married or widowed. Among couples, they marry less and cohabit more. They tend to be younger and to have more children. They are less well educated and have fewer qualifications. They are more often found in unskilled jobs, including the most routine non manual jobs. More than anything, though, they tend to be social tenants rather than owner occupiers, usually in council housing.

3   Smoking Among Low Income Families

Introduction
The reason for the lack of research complained of in *Her Share of Misfortune* is that reliable national samples that include low income families and ask questions about both material circumstances and smoking, are limited to surveys like the General Household Survey and the Family Expenditure Survey. Though large enough for their purposes, 10,000 and 7,000 households respectively, they never provided sufficient cases in the relatively small target groups of interest to unpack all the kinds of information needs described above. For this reason, what has long been suspected to be high smoking prevalence among very low income families tend to be masked in wider aggregations of all low income groups, and defined in terms of traditional measures of social class.

Occasionally, glimpses were visible in earlier years of the GHS and FES that there might be a special problem among the most disadvantaged groups. In addition, Marsh and Matheson's 1980 national study of 4,000 smokers hinted at a high smoking prevalence among what were then a smaller population of half a million lone parents. The 1990 General Household Survey report showed that 54 per cent of married men aged 16-24 and who had dependent children smoked cigarettes regularly, compared with 33 per cent of those who were unmarried with no children. Lone parenthood in women and early married parenthood in men, are both heavily associated with low family incomes.

Other studies, typically Hilary Graham's studies. Jones (1988), Simms and Smith (1986) and Madeley, Gillies and Power (1989) also found high prevalence of smoking among samples of working class mothers.

New data from the General Household Survey
One of the more striking achievements of the GHS has been to document the decline in smoking prevalence since 1970. The main points of the

findings were discussed in Chapter 1. On the other hand, the sole measure of social grade used to disaggregate the smoking data was social class. This showed important differences but, during this same period, allocation to social class by the occupation of the head of household tended to say less and less about equivalent family income.

One reason why income is rarely used in GHS analysis is that it is obtained only by a single scaled measure and it attracts a lot of refusals to answer. More than a fifth of GHS respondents do not answer the income questions and these seem to be the better off families. However, we felt strongly that we should check four things that our survey of low income families with children could not show.

1. Do low *income* families with children smoke more than higher income families, as the class differences would imply?
2. Do low income families *with children* smoke more or less compared with low income families without children?
3. Do the low income families with children *in our survey* smoke more or less compared with low income families in the GHS?
4. Have low income families *failed to reduce* their smoking prevalence at the same rate as higher income families?

Table 3.1 was provided by OPCS who carried out a special analysis of smoking prevalence using income instead of social class as an independent variable. The measure of income divides respondents into successively higher quarters among respondents aged 16 to 44.

The answers to our first two questions are seen plainly in Table 3.1. Low income families are more likely to smoke than higher income families; and by a huge margin. Comparing the four income quarters among married men with dependent children, half the lowest quarter smoke cigarettes regularly. This figure sheds 10 points as each successive income quarter is reached, so that less than a quarter of the highest income quarter smoke. The same gradient is seen among married women: from nearly half of those in the lowest income quarter smoking, down to less than a fifth among the highest quarter.

So the bad news was there all the time; among families with children, smoking prevalence rises steeply as income falls. Actually the *majority* of lone parents smoke: six out of ten of them. Half of lone fathers smoke. These figures for low income families' smoking are far higher than the social class gradient alone would predict.

Table 3.1 examines only adults in the GHS who are less than 45 years old. Another table (not shown here) that compares smoking among households with and without dependent children for all age groups, shows that there is almost no income gradient in smoking prevalence. This is because all-adult households are dominated by female pensioners who have low incomes and, for the moment, a low incidence of smoking. This is why the age range of Table 3.1 is restricted to 16 to 44 years. Here we see that a similar income gradient exists among adults under 44 who have no children living with them, except that women in the lowest income quarter who have neither partners nor children, are significantly less likely to smoke compared with those who have both, and far less likely than are the lone mothers.

The third question will be examined below when we present the data from our own survey. Meanwhile, Table 3.1 was recreated from GHS data for 1976, 1980, and 1986. The results are shown in Figure 3.1. They could hardly be clearer:

Better off families, with and without children, have reduced their smoking prevalence by half: from over 4 in 10 smoking in 1976 to just over 2 in 10 in 1990. Most of this fall occurred in the early to mid 1980s at a time, paradoxically in our view, when their real incomes were rising very quickly.

Families in the lowest income quarter have not changed their smoking at all. More than half of them smoked in 1976. More than half of them smoke now. Six out of ten lone parents smoked in 1976, six out of ten in 1990.

The excess in smoking attributable to membership of the lowest income quarter, compared with the highest, increased five-fold in 16 years.

Whatever has been the contribution of price policy to the reduction in smoking prevalence among families who are not poor, one thing is certain: it has had no effect at all upon families who are poor, except perhaps to stop it increasing. Let us look now in more detail; who among poor families smokes?

23

Figure 3.1 Changes in Smoking Prevalence, 1976–1990, by income quarter and family type, among respondents aged 16–44

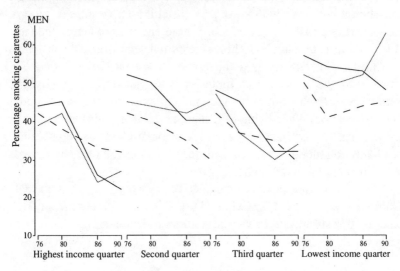

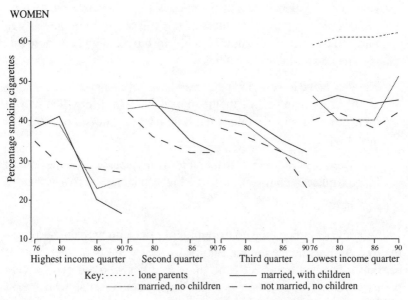

Key: ······· lone parents   ——— married, with children
   ············· married, no children   – – not married, no children

Source: General Household Survey

Table 3.1 Prevalence of cigarette smoking by sex and marital status by whether household includes dependent children by gross household income quarter: PERSONS AGED 16–44 ONLY.

	Per cent who smoke cigarettes regularly (cell percentages)							
	Men				Women			
Income	Partnered		No partner		Partnered		No partner	
Quarter	Children	No child	Children	No child	Children	No child	Children	No child
Lowest	48	(63)	...	51	45	51	62	42
Second	40	45	...	29	32	40	(48)	32
Third	32	34	...	29	28	29	...	23
Highest	22	27	...	32	17	25	...	27
Total	36	37	(50)	36	30	32	60	32
Bases:								
Lowest	299	49	13	311	331	53	346	244
Second	403	144	6	262	435	157	46	194
Third	383	195	4	216	427	217	16	186
Highest	298	200	1	352	357	231	6	203
Total	1383	588	24	1141	1550	658	414	827

Source: General Household Survey 1990 (unpublished)
Population: persons aged 16–44 (4915 are missing because there was no value given for household income.)
... = base too small for percentages.

Evidence from the DSS/PSI survey of low income families
In the following analysis of our own survey, the 46 per cent who are lone parent families are treated separately from the remainder, who are couples with children. Table 3.2 provides the basic information on smoking and marital status.

Family type
More than half (55 per cent) of the lone parents smoked cigarettes regularly, smoking an average of 15.6 cigarettes a day. Among the couples, somewhat fewer smoked: 38 per cent of women and 46 per cent of men. We are, therefore, showing slightly lower prevalence figures than

the GHS. This is because the GHS figures constructed income quarters on the basis of families' total incomes without regard to family composition. Our survey identified the lowest quarter in the *relative* income distribution among families with children. So our families are somewhat better off than those in the lowest quarter of the GHS distribution and, under the rule that the poorest smoke the most, the poor families in the GHS smoke more.

In terms of consumption, which we will look at much closer in the next chapter, the married women smoked exactly the same average numbers of cigarettes each day as the lone parents (15.6) while the men smoked a little more. These are about average figures.

If smokers and non-smokers were randomly allocated among couples, only 1 in 6 couples would have both partners smoking. But smokers tended to live with smokers, so 1 in 4 couples among low income families had both partners smoking, a third had one partner smoking, and only 4 out of 10 had neither partner smoking. This has implications for their children.

More than half the children living in low income families (57 per cent) lived with at least one adult smoker. This compares with about a third of children of all families according to the GHS. The proportion of children in low income families living with *two* adult smokers was probably about double the national average. This is to say nothing about the probability that they had older siblings smoking in the household, or, of course, that the children themselves smoked (cf OPCS Lader and Matheson, 1991)

Among these low income families, there appears to be a strong association simply between marital status and smoking. For example, couples divided sharply between those who were cohabiting and those who were married. Cohabiting women were nearly twice as likely to smoke as married women. Among men, this difference was narrower: 58 per cent among the cohabiting men, 44 per cent among the married men. Married low income parents continuing to live together, especially the married women, smoked little more than might be expected from national prevalence figures from the GHS, while those cohabiting without formal unions were far more likely to smoke. This association is not easily visible among the whole population because married and unmarried people have a similar smoking prevalence.

Table 3.2 Smoking and marital status

Lone Parents:

	Single	Separated from cohabitation	Separated from marriage	Divorced	Widowed	All
Per Cent Smoking	56%	67%	52%	47%	22%	55%

Couples:

	Women			Men		
	Cohabiting	Married	All	Cohabiting	Married	All
Per Cent Smoking	59%	36%	38%	59%	41%	43%

	Cohabiting %	Married %	All %
Neither smoke	25	45	42
She alone smokes	17	15	15
He alone smokes	16	20	19
Both smoke	43	21	23
	100	100	100

The link between marital status and smoking was echoed among lone parents. Widows were unlikely to smoke, divorced lone parents rather more likely to smoke, but single and separated lone parents more likely still. In fact, lone parents separated from a cohabitation were most likely to smoke: two thirds of them smoked cigarettes regularly compared with 54 per cent among those separated from a marriage, but not yet divorced. These rates were also matched by the 5 per cent of lone parents who were lone fathers: 65 per cent smoked cigarettes regularly and more than 8 out of 10 single and separated lone fathers smoked.

Thus, it appears that the further a low income parent was removed from the traditional form of co-resident marriage, the more likely she or he was to smoke. Broadly, those never legally married were about twice as likely to smoke as those currently married and living together. But current circumstances counted for more than past, except in the rarer case

27

of widows. For example: those currently divorced or separated from a marriage tended more towards the higher smoking prevalence of the never married and away from the lower prevalence of the still married.

Income
These differences by marital status are so large among low income families as to raise at once the question of whether the higher smoking prevalence observed for low income groups generally has less to do with their incomes per se and more to do with their broader social and material circumstances. This is exactly the right question to ask of low income families because their incomes, even in work, are so often linked to benefit rules. This means that their incomes are partly standardised on the numbers of their children, so many low income families have quite similar *equivalent* incomes. The majority of lone parents have the same equivalent income.

It is also difficult to consider income because housing costs are met out of work but not in work, except for some residual housing benefit for the lowest income working families alongside their family credit. Table 3.3 shows the simplest comparison, looking at differences in smoking prevalence between families on different levels of *disposal* income, that is, their total family income minus their actual housing costs. The weighted cell sizes are included to show the relative sizes of each income stratum; this is important.

Table 3.3 Prevalence by disposable income: per cent who smoke (cell percentages)

	Disposable Income				
	Up to £50	£51–100	£101 –150	£151 –200	Over 200
Lone parents	48	57	55	<— 37 —>	
(Weighted N=)	(162)	(1010)	(351)	(147)	
Couples					
She smokes	40	44	37	36	37
He smokes	45	66	47	38	40
Both smoke	25	34	26	19	21
(Weighted N=)	(101)	(266)	(518)	(410)	(304)

The results in Table 3.3 are equivocal. Lone parents who had higher income were significantly less likely to smoke, but they were only about 1 in 10 of all low income lone parents. Among the remaining bulk of lone parents, uniformly more than half smoked. Among married women, the proportion smoking was the same regardless of the level of family income. Among their husbands, there was a striking concentration of smoking among those low, but not the lowest incomes. This, as we shall see below, is more strongly connected to the source of their family income than its amount: they were on income support.

This is an important result. It means that any differences between the welfare of smokers that we shall investigate in the next chapter are unlikely to be due to large differences in current cash incomes. In fact, smokers and non-smokers had quite similar incomes:

	Lone parents		Couples			
	Smokers	Non-smokers	Both smoke	He smokes	She smokes	Neither smoke
Average income	86	93	144	134	150	155
Median income	77	83	123	134	152	150

£s per week

Family size

Numbers of children in a family appeared unrelated to smoking prevalence. Those with four or more children were no more likely to smoke than those with just one. But among lone parents, there was some tendency for those with younger children to be more likely to smoke, especially if the children were under 5. However, this is in turn related to greater numbers of single and separated lone parents being more likely to have the younger children and to smoke more.

This, together with the relatively weak link with incomes, suggests an interesting conclusion. The two factors that are most often associated with family poverty and with smoking: having a low family income and larger numbers of children, do not then contribute the main explanation for increased levels of smoking *within* the population of low income families. (Berthoud and Kempson found a similar result for the incidence of problem debt.) There will be some remaining connection with income, but other factors are likely to be more important.

Ethnic group
There is a persistent finding in the literature (see for example Graham 1989) that, in Britain at least, Black and Asian women are noticeably less likely to smoke, despite being more likely to be counted among low income groups. This is certainly the evidence among this sample of low income families (Table 3.4).

We interviewed 108 Asian women; 4 of them smoked, each of them married. Not a single Asian lone parent smoked. All were widows and they were an important reason why so few widows in the sample as a whole smoked. Among Asian couples, less than a fifth of the men smoked. Both Asian partners smoked in only one case compared with a quarter of white couples. More Black (that is mainly Afro-Caribbean) lone mothers smoked, but still only a third of them compared with 56 per cent of white lone mothers.

Table 3.4 Prevalence by ethnic group

% who smoke	White	Asian	Black	'Other'
Lone parents	56	0	33	(54)
Couples				
Women	40	7	(12)	(4)
Men	44	17	(43)	(18)
Both smoke	24	1	(12)	(4)

Housing tenure
We wrote in the previous chapter about the importance of housing tenure in creating new and growing divisions among families, even among low income families, and its effects on their well being. Its effects on their smoking are equally dramatic.

Families in social tenancies (mostly local authority tenants plus a few housing association tenants) are about twice as likely to smoke compared with owner occupiers (Table 3.5). On the crucial measure of both members of a couple smoking, the difference is even greater (14 per cent vs 33 per cent).

This is the magnitude of difference that might be expected in a general population sample, rather than a sample of low income families. General population surveys will contain many professional owner occupiers whose smoking prevalence is nowadays down to about 15 per cent. It is less easily understood in a sample comprising families who are all in the lowest quarter of the income distribution. A difference that in the general population would be attributed easily to differences in occupation and income status, education and life-style choices, and so on between tenants and owners, looks among this sample much more like a *primary* difference: that there is a direct relationship between tenure and health behaviour, unmediated by traditional class differences of occupation and wealth. We will look at the extent of combined effects shortly. Meanwhile, another, simpler aspect of housing also has its effects: size.

Among lone parents, 60 per cent were social tenants and a third of these lived in flats, two thirds in semi-detached or terraced houses, a few in detached council houses. Two thirds of the flat dwellers smoked compared with half those living in houses. Similar differences occurred among couples, though more narrowly.

This too has implications for children. The internal volumes of council flats are not great, far lower than those inhabited by the great majority of children, even among low income families, who live in houses. The 4 out of 10 children of social tenant couples living with two smoking adults must be very high volume secondary smokers, even if they do not themselves smoke. Fewer than 1 in 5 council flat-dwelling children lived in smoke free flats. Similar effects apply to those living in privately rented accommodation, though these are a much smaller group.

Table 3.5 Prevalence by tenure (all low income families)

| | Cell percentages | | | |
	Owner occupier	Social tenants	Private tenants	Other
Lone parents	37	60	60	41
Couples				
Women	27	52	42	21
Men	33	55	41	35
Both smoke	14	33	26	13

Work

The account in the previous chapter of patterns of work among low income families stressed that their economic activity is not dominated by traditional forms of manual work. There are a number of reasons for this that are important for our story:

- low income work has changed, embracing many routine non-manual jobs in shops, offices and service industries
- the definition of low *family incomes* includes many larger families who have more than the lowest incomes
- many of them are women's jobs; again, low paid non-manual work.

There are however, some important differences that are associated with work (Table 3.6).

First, simply being in work was only weakly associated with lower smoking prevalence, especially among married men. Fewer of those who were economically active (ie. in work, or unemployed and seeking work) smoked cigarettes regularly compared with those wholly out of work, or working a few part time hours each week. This is an interesting finding because, especially for lone parents, it seems reasonable to suppose that the stresses and strains of balancing home, children and a full time job would add to stress in ways that might increase smoking. But it does not; it was those at home with their children, nearly all of them living on income support, who were significantly more likely to smoke. But the differences were not large: 58 per cent of lone parents at home with their children smoked compared with 47 per cent of those in full time work.

On the other hand, two-thirds of the quite large group of unemployed men smoked compared with 4 out of 10 of men in full time work. And, although married women at home with children were not more likely to smoke compared with those few in work, those whose *husbands* were unemployed were themselves more likely to smoke (46 per cent compared with 33 per cent).

Occupation, or former occupation among those who have had paid work in the past three years, was also significantly associated with smoking. (Table 3.7)

The effects were strongest among lone parents. Those doing unskilled manual jobs were twice as likely to smoke compared with those in professional or other non-manual jobs, except retail and service work: a difference of a third compared with two thirds smoking cigarettes regularly. But even these differences concealed some wider differences among the lone parents in manual work. Those in the least prestigious occupations: unskilled assembly workers, catering (probably lots of school cooks), cleaners, and distribution workers had among them an extraordinarily high prevalence of smoking. For example, out of 594 lone parents who were in work or had had jobs in the past three years, 56 were catering staff; 46 of them smoked: a prevalence of 82 per cent.

This is the kind of finding that is invisible to even large scale whole population surveys, or, when such figures are found in local studies, tend to be seen as having been sought out as special cases of interest.

Table 3.6 Smoking by economic activity

Cell percentages

	Lone parents			Couples		
	In work	Not in work	Both work	She works He does not	He works She does not	Neither work
Per cent who smoke	50	56				
Women:			35	40	32	46
Men:			40	49	39	57
Both Smoke:			22	31	19	32

The relationship between occupation and smoking among couples is not as dramatic as it is among some lone parents, but as a general rule, smoking was significantly more common among manual workers compared with non-manual workers, with the service sector workers in between. Smoking among the husbands showed a particularly uneven pattern. For example, only a third of the junior and intermediate non-manual employees were smokers compared with more than half those in retail and personal service jobs.

On the other hand, it is worth remembering that whole population surveys find very low prevalence figures among professional and higher non-manual groups: down nowadays to about 15 per cent. Among these low income families, smoking among professional and higher non-manual groups was higher: about a third among lone parents and a quarter among couples. So there is a residual effect associated with being a low income family.

Table 3.7 Smoking by occupational classification

Lone Parents					
	Professional managerial	Junior non-manual	Retail & service	Skilled manual	Unskilled manual
Per cent who smoke:	37	33	51	60	67

Couples (women, own occupational group)					
	Professional managerial	Junior non-manual	Retail & service	Skilled manual	Unskilled manual
Per cent who smoke:	23	27	40	37	45

Couples (men, own occupational group)					
	Professional managerial	Junior non-manual	Retail & service	Skilled manual	Unskilled manual
Per cent who smoke:	29	45	51	43	44

Couples (men and women, men's occupational group)					
	Professional managerial	Junior non-manual	Retail & service	Skilled manual	Unskilled manual
Per cent of families where both smoke:	13	20	28	21	28

Work and benefits

Chapter 2 described how the design of the study brought into sharp focus the lowest 5 per cent of the family income distribution by oversampling family credit recipients. On one side of these were placed the out of work families (though some did a little part time work) and on the other side the moderate income families. Alongside the family credit families are the 'eligible non-claimants' – the families who qualify for family credit but do not claim it. Table 3.8 shows the prevalence of smoking within each group.

A familiar pattern emerged. On one side, significantly, more of the 'benefit families' (either working and claiming family credit or not working and getting income support) smoked cigarettes regularly compared with the moderate income families. Among women, the eligible non-claimants shared the appropriately moderate smoking prevalence of the moderate income families. Among men, it was the out of work men claiming income support and unemployment benefit who were significantly more likely to smoke.

Table 3.8 Prevalence by 'income-benefit status'

Per cent who smoke					
		Working and ...			
	Out of work	Claim family credit	Eligible non-claimants	Moderate income	Highest income
Lone parents	57	53	40	38	33
Couples					
Women	45	43	34	31	na
Men	55	46	48	39	na
Both smoke	29	26	24	20	na

These differences were not large, not as large as those associated with tenure or marital status. This is because low income families tend to move between different benefit status groups quite rapidly. The real difference tended to lie in their benefit histories rather than their present status. For example, the highest smoking prevalence was found among the small groups of families who recently were working and claiming family credit but were discovered in the survey slipping out of work and back onto income support. Among out of work couples, smoking was nearly twice as common among the former family credit families compared with those who had never claimed family credit. Likewise, couples who had any experience of claiming income support *now or in the past* were twice as likely to be dual smoking couples compared with those who had never had to claim income support.

On the other hand, this was not true of the moderate income families. Only 17 per cent of them had ever had to claim income support and they were not more likely to smoke compared with other moderate income families who had never claimed income support.

Among the families currently claiming income support, the amount of time they had remained claimants was not significantly related to their smoking, except among lone parents. The significantly large group who had remained on income support for more than 5 years (nearly a fifth of all lone parents) reported 69 per cent of them as smokers compared with a half of other lone parents on IS.

Table 3.8 also includes about 100 'highest income' lone parents. These were a special sample of lone parents whose incomes exceeded our definition of low income families but who were interviewed for another purpose. Exactly a third of them smoked. This may seem unsurprising except when, again, one remembers that nearly all of them are well paid professionals. In the population as a whole, professional women (or wives of professional men) smoke least: about 16 per cent of them smoke. The earlier observation of a third of low income lone parent professionals smoking might have been doubted, since low income professionals are not in the traditional way of professional work. But these higher income (some of them very high income) lone parents show that there is a strong residual effect associated with marital status. There is something irreducible about being a lone parent that, other things being equal, increases the likelihood of being a smoker.

Education
Given the above results associating higher levels of smoking with the least skilled jobs, it is reasonable to expect an association between educational qualifications and smoking. Again this is of special interest among families who have fairly similar incomes, since the low smoking rates among the best educated in the population as a whole are associated at the same time with a modern middle class lifestyle in which smoking seems more and more rejectable.

Once more, the lone parents told the clearest story. About two thirds of those with no qualifications, or who had one of a range of miscellaneous and minor vocational certificates, smoked cigarettes regularly. So did more than half those with CSEs, RSAs or City and Guilds. In fact, only among those who had A Level or higher qualifications did the number smoking fall to the lower levels nowadays associated with the better educated. Even so, some will wonder at the figure of 4 out of 10 lone parent nurses smoking (though, obeying the lone parent doubling rule, only 2 out of 10 married nurses smoked).

In general, couples showed similar patterns. The least educated married women numbered twice the proportion of smokers among them compared to the best educated. Among men the proportion of smokers fell from about a half among those without qualifications to about a third of those with A levels or better. These last, however, are only about 15 per cent among low income parents.

Combined effects

It is already clear in this analysis that, like of lot of other things among low income families, smoking follows the 'benefit fault line'. On the one side are the family credit and income support claimants, living in council accommodation, accustomed to manual or service sector work, and who smoke. On the other side are those who do not claim benefits, live in inexpensive owner occupied accommodation, usually found in non-manual work, and who do not smoke.

This is a generalisation, and there are exceptions. But how effective a generalisation is it? And does it hold equally for lone parents and for couples?

In more detail, the generalisation is as follows: higher smoking prevalence among low income families is strongly associated with being a white lone parent, having no educational qualifications, being a council tenant, a manual or former manual worker and claiming means tested social security benefits. It might as well be said now that the minority of women who have all of these characteristics share a smoking prevalence of 87 per cent. Among married women who also share this set of disadvantages, prevalence is lower unless they also have a partner who smokes, when it is similar. Thus it seems that increased smoking among low income families, compared to the better off majority, is not something that is a general product of having low income and children. It is an effect that is linked into *degrees of disadvantage*.

But what is doing all this? All these markers of disadvantage are strongly linked to one another, as was so clearly seen in the last chapter. Even so, do these components of disadvantage have an independent effect on smoking or is it really a single effect that could be represented equally well by any one measure?

Too many measures appear strongly to influence smoking prevalence to be able to show all these combined effects in tabular form. So to answer this question we turned to a statistical procedure called logistic regression. It is similar in procedure to the more familiar multiple regression programmes but uses odds-ratio estimates rather than least squares. For this reason it is suitable for use with a dependent variable that is a dichotomy: do you smoke or not? The version used was that found in SPSSX.

Entered into the equation first were a series of dummy variables, counting for example as 'yes' or 'no' whether or not a respondent was a council tenant, housing association tenant, a private tenant, or living with parents. There were 65 of these dummy variables and it is unrewarding to try to show clearly in a report intended for wide readership how all these fared. However, following procedures that allowed for progressive simplification, seeking, as it is said, the most parsimonious model, it is possible to show equations that capture most of the explanation for smoking by a few dichotomous measures.

Table 3.9 summarises these 'most parsimonious' equations in a form that is most easily interpretable. The change in odds-ratio estimates associated with the impact of each factor on smoking has been converted into a percentage probability, relative to the probability that a 'reference person' smokes. Our reference lone parent is white, divorced, a social tenant on income support, has done non-manual work and has educational qualification. There is a 43 per cent chance that she smokes. Our reference couple are similar, except that they are married, and they share a 27 per cent probability that they both smoke.

First, it is striking that ethnicity is a constantly significant feature throughout. All other things held constant, being Black or Asian reduces smoking among low income families, especially lone parents. Thus there are independent cultural reasons why Black and Asian low income parents have a very low smoking prevalence. The strangest aspect of this important finding is that it runs counter to the message emerging from every other aspect of the data. Being Black or Asian among low income families is a marker for additional disadvantage, except that Asian families tend to be owner-occupiers. Ethnicity, therefore, is the one factor that points to a low of incidence smoking among some of the most disadvantaged families. To do this, it is an extremely powerful effect.

Beyond ethnicity, and beyond lone parenthood itself, there are four factors that are consistently and independently important in raising smoking prevalence: being a tenant, claiming income support, having no educational qualifications and doing or having recently done manual work.

Among lone parents this is an extremely clear result. The influence of claiming social security benefits disappeared when tenure, work and education were held constant. This is partly because so very many of them claimed benefits, two thirds claimed income support and a third of the remainder claimed family credit. There is also a complicating factor in that lone parents (and many married women too) were often so far removed from the labour market that simply being able to classify them as manual or nonmanual workers restricts the analysis to those with present or recent work experience, whom we know were anyway less likely to smoke. In this way 'claiming income support' is a surrogate for saying you are not in work. 15 per cent of lone parents had never had a proper job.

Table 3.9 Logistic regression analysis predicting smoking.

Lone Parents	Reference person is a low income white lone parent who is a tenant, receiving income support, has some educational qualifications and did non-manual work when employed, and she is divorced.

	Probability of being a smoker
Non-white	24%
Owner occupier	32%
Not on income support	40%
Reference lone parent	**43%**
Single, never married	55%
Manual worker	59%
No qualifications	59%
Manual work and no qualifications	74%

Couples	Reference couple are white, tenants, do non-manual work when they can but are now on income support, they are married and one of them has some educational qualifications.

	Probability of being a couple who both smoke
Owner occupiers	17%
Not on income support	18%
Reference couple	**23%**
Woman has no qualifications	35%
Cohabiting	44%
Cohabiting and woman has no educational qualifications	53%

Among couples the range of prediction is similar: tenure, benefit receipt, marital status and education, especially the mother's education, combine to raise the probability of both smoking by a factor of three.

Table 3.10 presents the simplest division of lone parents into tenants and owner occupiers, those with educational qualifications and those with none, and those who were manual or nonmanual workers.

Table 3.10 Combined effects

(Percent who smoke)				
a. Lone parents	Owner occupiers		Social tenants	
	Qualifications	No qualifications	Qualifications	No qualifications
Non-manual	29	49	37	72
Manual	44	66	71	69
No recent work	42	30	50	61

b. Couples	Owner occupiers		Social tenants	
	Qualifications	No qualifications	Qualifications	No qualifications
Women				
On Income Support or Family Credit	28	29	48	55
Not on Income Support or Family Credit	22	30	35	49
Men				
On Income Support or Family Credit	36	35	53	69
Not on Income Support or Family Credit	33	37	45	51
Both				
On Income Support or Family Credit	21	15	33	43
Not on Income Support or Family Credit	14	16	23	29

Lone parents who had none of these three aspect of disadvantage – owner occupiers, nonmanual or former nonmanual workers and had some educational qualifications – were no more likely to smoke than women generally. Though again we would need to compare them with young women in the general population who had their own homes, qualifications and did nonmanual work to be sure there was no residual increase in smoking due to lone parenthood. Evidence discussed earlier suggests that there is such a remaining effect.

Lone parents who had any one of these aspects of disadvantage were more likely to smoke – approaching half of them smoked. Those who had two or three such aspects were more likely still to smoke: at least two thirds of them.

It is particularly interesting that a lack of educational qualifications increased the likelihood of smoking independently of other factors *including whether or not they had experience of manual work.* A similar effect, though less strong is observable among married women too. This is partly because as shown in the previous chapter, only a minority of even the most disadvantaged women now do what is strictly classified as manual work. It was usually poorly paid work, but not strictly 'manual'.

Education might be tapping another dimension that has something to do with personal resourcefulness and understanding. But education has become a structural factor too. Among low income families, it is possible to say that being entirely unqualified is becoming a more important precursor of the kinds of social and economic disadvantage now associated with smoking, than manual work ever was. It is strongly associated with lone parenthood, for example.

Those who left school in the 1970s and 1980s without a qualification to their name were a much smaller group than among earlier cohorts in the 1950s and 1960s, especially the young women. But half of this sample of low income parents were unqualified school-leavers, men and women alike. They represented a new kind of early clustering of young people who faced multiple disadvantage in a changing labour market. They found themselves on the fringes of the economy far more clearly and much earlier than those destined for lower working class life in earlier decades. In the 1970s, unqualified school-leavers gathered in numbers in prematurely ageing council estates. They became socially and geographically differentiated from qualified school leavers elsewhere. They created a protected habitat for high levels of smoking that have not been seen elsewhere since the early 1960s. When our study found them in 1991, they had become the poorest among Britain's low income parents. And they were still smoking.

Among couples, similar patterns of multiple influence on smoking were seen but social tenancy tended to dominate other effects to some extent. Manual work also exerted less influence, independently of other factors, as did cohabitation rather than marriage. But among couples, unlike lone parents, receiving benefits became independently important. Strangely though, married women's probability of being a smoker was raised by receiving family credit, men's by receiving income support.

However, the further complicating factor among couples was that, again quite independently of the basic background factors such as housing tenure, work and education, still by far the largest increase in prevalence was associated with having a partner who smokes.

This is important because it means that dual smoking in low income families – those for whom the expenditure problem will be significantly the largest – share their smoking habits for reasons above and beyond shared disadvantage.

There are a number of reasons why this might be so. They may select one another more readily as partners in the first place, of course. And it is so much more difficult to contemplate giving up if your partner, especially your partner in disadvantage, constantly reinforces your habit for you. Women separated from a marriage had similar rates of smoking compared to married women, and divorced women had lower rates. It would be interesting to know whether women who separate from husbands who smoked subsequently find it easier to give up, lone parenthood notwithstanding.

Evidence from the National Child Development Study

NCDS has its origins in the National Birthday Trust Fund's Perinatal Mortality Survey in 1958. The 17,000 children born in one week in March of that year are the original sample. It was the purpose of the PMS to study the social as well as the obstetric cause of stillbirth and neonatal death and so a considerable amount of data was gathered on the social and economic circumstances of the infants' families.

The cohort study was started by the National Children's Bureau when they carried out a survey of 16,500 of the PMS families when the children became seven in 1965 and continued with further surveys at age 11, 16 and 23. The childhood surveys gathered data about the parents' work, family, housing and other social and economic circumstances, including limited amounts of financial information, as well as developmental data for the children themselves. At 23, a full range of social and economic data was gathered about the cohort members and focused on the transition to adulthood. Secondary data sources were also added, including the cohort's CSE and GCE examination results.

A new survey, called 'NCDS-5', was carried out in 1991, when the cohort became 33 years old. Seventy percent of the original cohort were interviewed – nearly 11,500 people. This survey too gathered a wide range of social and economic information about the 1958 cohort members, who were all 33 years old when interviewed in 1991.

Smoking has always been an important aspect of NCDS. It was the first study to show conclusively that smoking in pregnancy harmed the foetus and went on to show that the harm was lasting throughout childhood. Smoking was included in NCDS5, present, past and partner's too.

Table 3.11 Smoking among the 1958 cohort, by income quartile sex and marital status and parenthood.

Cell percentages: per cent who smoke					
	Men			Women	
	Two-parent family	Not parent	Lone parent family	Two-parent family	Not parent
Income quintile					
Lowest	42	49	53	37	45
Second	35	39	60	32	38
Third	27	36	↑	28	36
Fourth	26	32	48	23	31
Fifth	23	29	↓	21	21

The figures in Table 3.11 are entirely consistent with the GHS data in Table 3.1. Whereas some of the high levels of smoking among those with the lowest incomes may have been due to young people smoking and not yet giving up, we see undiminished income difference in smoking prevalence at 33 years old. But again we can ask the question, what is important, income itself or social disadvantage?

The answer seems clear: it is social disadvantage. For example: social tenants are twice as likely to smoke compared with owner occupiers and this is true at each level of income: social tenants with above average incomes are twice as likely to smoke as owner occupiers with *below* average incomes. Housing tenure combines with education to wipe out the effects of income entirely. Social tenants with no educational qualifications are nearly four times more likely to smoke compared with owner occupiers who have 'A' levels or better (Table 3.12)

Table 3.12 Smoking in the 1958 cohort by sex, tenure and educational qualifications.

Cell percentages

	Men		Women	
	Owner	Council	Owner	Council
No Qualifications	43	67	47	68
CSE	40	59	35	57
Around O levels	29	55	26	51
A levels or better	18	51	18	53

On the other hand, education seems to have a really significant impact on reducing prevalence only among the owner occupiers. True, these were the great majority: nearly eight out of ten cohort members were owner occupiers. Better educated council tenants were still far more likely to smoke, even compared with less well educated owner occupiers. Among couples with children, half the unqualified council tenants were in couples who both smoked. Only a quarter of their children lived in homes where neither parent smoke compared with 8 out of ten children in owner occupied homes where one or both parents had 'A' levels or better.

This again raises the question of social geography. In NCDS we were able to identify those young families who in the past few years had bought their homes from their local authority under the right-to-buy scheme. They still live in the same milieu as the continuing tenants. And they still smoke; not as much as the continuing tenants, but far more than those who bought their homes in the open market (Table 3.13)

Table 3.13 Smoking in the 1958 cohort by housing tenure and type of vendor.

Tenure	Cell percentages: per cent who smoke			
	Own outright	Buying on mortgage	Private tenant	Council tenant
	24	27	42	59
All owners	Bought from…			
	Developer	Private	Housing association	Council
	18	25	34	44

NCDS allows us to piece together each cohort member's past in order to try to answer some of the questions raised by the analysis of the survey of low income families. Some of the most important of these concerned lone parenthood. There were over 400 lone parents in NCDS5 but there were more than 600 who were lone parents at some time during the previous 16 years, but now had a new partner or, in some cases, their first.

Table 3.14 Smoking in the 1958 cohort by type of lone parent experience.

	Separated from marriage	Divorced	Separated from cohabitation	Single	New family	No child
	%	%	%	%	%	%
Never smoked	34	35	27	40	32	20
Smoke now	47	53	57	49	53	65
Gave up	19	12	16	11	12	15
	100					
Bases	181	264	63	43	611	51

Table 3.15 Smoking in the 1958 cohort by age of first lone parenting and subsequent status.

Became a lone parent at	16–20 and		21–25 and		25–33 and	
	Still lone parent	Not lone parent	Still lone parent	Not lone parent	Still lone parent	Not lone parent
	%	%	%	%	%	%
Never smoked	20	30	28	25	37	37
Smoke now	74	56	59	58	47	48
Gave up	6	14	13	17	15	15
	100					
Bases	50	142	102	204	318	274

There was little difference in smoking between lone parents who had or had not had partners in the past. But, long term, forming a new family was associated with giving up smoking. Eight out of ten of those who became lone parents in their teens and were still lone parents at 33 smoked and only a handful gave up. Of those who found partners, fewer started and more gave up; though still half of them smoked (Tables 3.14 and 3.15). Otherwise re-partnering made little difference. One of their problems was that they tended to marry smokers. Even in the highest income group, a quarter of new family couples both smoked; in the lowest, four out of ten. But their circumstances still made a difference. Seven out of ten former lone parents smoked if their new family was on income support.

If being a lone parent is of itself an important reason to smoke, and it seems clear that it is regardless of other circumstances, then being an absent parent has exactly the same effect. We were able to identify over 600 cohort members who had had children born to them but were living apart from them, most of them men of course. Overall, they were about twice as likely to smoke compared with the great majority who were not absent parents. Among those who lived alone, prevalence rose to nearly 70 per cent.

Among cohort members who had not had the unsettling experiences of being either a lone parent or an absent parent, we looked carefully for signs that improvements in standards of living may be associated with giving up smoking. Table 3.15 identifies cohort members who had had at least one spell claiming income support or supplementary benefit, and those who had never claimed and compares this with their present circumstances. At each level of present income, about 7 out of 10 had smoked cigarettes regularly at some time in their 33 years. Most had given up during their 20s. This of course co-incided with the period in the early 1980s when cessation was greatest among the better off groups generally.

Among the better off cohort members, half had given up smoking by 1991, but this was true whether or not they had had a spell on income support in the past. This held true even when those who had been students were excluded from the analysis on the ground that students in the early 1980s could still claim supplementary benefit if they needed to during the vacations. Even so, it is particularly interesting to have such clear evidence of large scale smoking cessation among better off young people during the 1980s. Among those prior claimants whose fortunes had not improved, half still smoked and only about a quarter had given up.

There is a simple point proved by the NCDS data that is of the first importance to our story: three-quarters of young people in all income groups take up regular smoking. Half of young smokers in middle and higher income groups give up by their early 30s. The poorest smokers do not give up. Their poverty, and its effect on them, stands in the way.

Table 3.15 Smoking in the 1958 cohort: present income by past experience of income support, two-parent families and those without children.

	Income quintile				
	1st	2nd	3rd	4th	5th
Two parent families					
Claimed Income Support in the past					
Per cent who smoke:	52	44	36	36	26
Ex-smokers as a					
percentage of ever-smokers:	25	29	39	39	48
Never claimed Income Support					
Per cent who smoke:	31	30	25	21	21
Ex-smokers as a					
percentage of ever-smokers:	38	41	48	49	52
Cohort members without children					
Claimed Income Support in the past					
Per cent who smoke:	50	45	39	41	26
Ex-smokers as a					
percentage of ever-smokers:	23	20	26	24	45
Never claimed Income Support					
Per cent who smoke:	45	35	34	28	26
Ex-smokers as a					
percentage of ever-smokers:	13	31	33	40	41

Conclusion

All this adds up to an extraordinary social and economic structuring of smoking in Britain at the moment. It is even more extraordinary how these structures are reproduced among low income families. It is particularly important to bear in mind that people who become parents and have low incomes are *not* automatically more likely to be smokers. If they get some educational qualifications, become low cost owner occupiers, stay together, take lower paid nonmanual work, and shun all contact with the Department of Social Security, they are probably no more likely to smoke than are other men and women who share a similar lifestyle, but who have either more money or no children. Their smoking prevalence is about one in five compared, among the rest of low income families, with 4 out of 10 of the married women, half the married men and more than half the lone parents. The problem is that such better provided families among low income families are actually quite rare: only 8 per cent of couples, 4 per cent of lone parents.

The risk of smoking among low income families appears to increase if they are lone parents, unless their former partner died. More probably, these risks of smoking, and with much else besides, rise when they appear among the ranks of Britain's low income families *as a consequence* of becoming a lone parent. This happens most commonly through separation and divorce. But nowadays there are rapidly increasing numbers who become lone parents though their first major step in adult life.

Indeed, comparing lone parents with mothers who keep their first union, or with young women who have no children, it seems possible to argue that the great increase in lone parenthood has contributed directly to the upward blip in smoking prevalence detected by the GHS among young women generally. Increasing lone parent numbers from 500,000 to 1.3 million in 10 years may have delivered at least 150,000 extra women smokers into the population who might not otherwise have become or remained smokers. That is about 6 per cent of women smokers aged 16 to 45.

Risks of smoking rise further if low income families are social tenants. Most of the elevation in smoking prevalence among low income families occurs among the two thirds of them who live as tenants of local authorities. More than half of them, of course, are lone parents. Add to this picture other elements of disadvantage, such as unemployment, a history of claiming means tested social security benefits in or out of work, and a record of work in manual labour (especially the least congenial jobs), then one enters areas of social existence where smoking among the parents of young children seems almost inescapable. It is not too fanciful to suggest that exploring this data set of low income families, once you are away from the minority of owner occupied homes, is a little like wandering around the newly emergent countries of Eastern Europe. Everyone seems poorly dressed, poorly housed, indifferently educated, unemployed or doing uncongenial work, most people appear to be still dependent on State support, and everyone smokes. Britain's lowest income families now maintain a milieu wherein smoking remains a norm. Its association with disadvantage is more and more identifying smoking as a compensation for disadvantage. Many lone parents identify smoking as their only compensation and they defend their habit assertively.

Strangely, the only thing that exempts low income families from this process, that is, a process that *cumulatively* associates increased smoking with increased disadvantage, is being Afro-caribbean and, especially, Asian. For the present at least, British Asian women with families seem somehow protected against smoking. Whether this will remain the case in succeeding generations will be interesting to know. And even more interesting to know why.

But for the rest, for the great majority of white socially-housed working class parents, these data have described a problem with smoking that has remained hidden from official statistics and, partly for that reason, from policy thought. Traditional sources such as the GHS used traditional social divisions that did not cut into the reality of people's lives in ways that might have connected with the new social distribution of smoking. This is not intended as a criticism of the ways the GHS and FES have used their data. For the mass of the population who do not have dependent children and low incomes, the more familiar social divisions are appropriate. The problem is that income has become detached from social class, especially among families with children. The majority of our low income families would have been classified as non-manual grades.

This study among a large sample of Britain's low income families has been able to describe the social aetiology of smoking among them using the measures that *acting in concert* shape their daily lives: marriage, relationships and children, ethnicity, housing, unemployment and social security, education, and what they do for a living when they have jobs. None of this can be constructed in the same way and at this level of detail from the traditional sources. There is something in these people's lives that is causing them to need to smoke, to expect to smoke, and not to give up. There seems only one possible candidate for this role: poverty. Poor smokers share an enduring lack of the means of good family provision and of social participation. They share the stress such lack brings, and the feelings of inequality, indeed, the fact of inequality, it means. They see the same lack of opportunity and the absence of optimism that accompany it. And they live with the hardship it brings. It is to this difficult question we turn in the next chapter.

4   The Effects of Smoking on Low Income Families

What does it cost?
Evidence from the Family Expenditure Survey
The report on the 1991 FES divides two parent families into four: those having 1, 2, 3 and 4 or more children, and divides one parent families into those with 1 and those with 2 or more children. Within the two parent families, expenditure data is shown separately for each approximate income quarter for those with 1 or 2 children and in successive thirds for those with 3 children. Thus it is possible to extract Table 4.1 for expenditure on tobacco products at the household level:

There are three important points in Table 4.1.

- The average lone parent spends two thirds as much on cigarettes as does the average couple with dependent children. Since we can superimpose the GHS lone parents' prevalence figure of 60 per cent upon the all-one-parent household expenditure figures, we can estimate that those who smoke spend more than £8 a week, or about 6 per cent of all their expenditure, on cigarettes. Lone parent smokers and non-smokers are unlikely to have the same total expenditure, so the true proportion is likely to be higher than 6 per cent.
- Spending on cigarettes is much higher among couples with four or more children. Such larger families (now only 8 per cent of all families) tend to have lower incomes than other families.
- Among smaller families, the table shows a very steep income gradient for spending, of the same order of magnitude as that shown by the GHS for prevalence: The poorest families spend twice as much on cigarettes than do the best off families.

Table 4.1 Expenditure on tobacco products by households with dependent children. (Average in £s per week per household) in 1991.

	Lone parents		Couples			
No. of children	1	2	1	2	3	4+
All families	4.77	4.40	6.70	5.68	6.58	8.09
Income quarter						
Lowest			8.74	9.41		
Second			6.65	5.91		
Third			7.06	4.65		
Highest			4.28	3.68		
Income group						
Lowest third					8.91	
Middle third					6.74	
Highest third					3.98	

Source: Family Spending in 1991, HMSO 1992, Table 11.

Table 4.2 Expenditure on tobacco products by households with dependent children. (Average in £s per week per household) in 1976.

	Lone parents	Couples			
Number of children	1 or more	1	2	3	4+
All families	1.36	2.37	2.52	2.66	3.31
Income					
Lowest		2.44	2.82		
	1.01	2.36	2.21		3.24
		2.49	2.82	2.39	
	1.42	2.25	2.47	2.73	
		2.27	2.96	2.93	
	1.55	2.41	2.23	2.22	
		2.46	2.58		3.37
Highest		2.19			

Source: *Family Expenditure Survey 1976*, HMSO, London, 1978, Tables 11 to 14.

As the earlier evidence from the General Household Survey would lead us to expect, an inspection of the Family Expenditure Survey for 1976 shows no significant income gradient. In fact, among lone parents, there was a sharp negative income gradient. But the same observation held for couples with children: those with four or more children spent more on tobacco than couples with fewer children and this was true of the better off large families too. So there is something about a house full of children that prompts parents to smoke, independently of their means. Such large families are now very rare.

Evidence from the DSS/PSI Survey of Low Income Families
Cigarette consumption among those who smoked, we said, was exactly the same among lone parents and married women: 15.6 cigarettes a day. It was a little higher among men: 17.4. Consumption among couples where either or both smoked was 23.6 cigarettes a day and when both smoked, it was 35 a day. These figures correspond closely with the national average consumption of people aged 25 to 49 (GHS, 1990)

These are average figures and represent a wide range of cigarette consumption. A third of couples who smoke, got through more than 25 a day and a fifth more than 35. Most of the greater amounts of smoking was reported among men, with 18 per cent smoking more than 20 a day. Married women and lone parents, on the other hand, showed some evidence of rationing their smoking, or at least 'capping' their expenditure. Fewer than one in ten of lone parents smoked more than 20 a day and almost none more than 30.

These consumption figures can be translated into expenditure by making a few reasonable assumptions. The average price of cigarettes in mid 1991 was £1.88 for 20. The very cheapest cigarettes, likely to be popular with our respondents, cost £1.49 for 20. We assumed that the average price paid was halfway between the cheapest and the average, which is £1.68 for 20.

The average amount spent on cigarettes by low income families who smoked, was estimated to be about £8.60 a week among the lone parents and £14.10 a week among couples. Because of the apparent capping of expenditure, particularly by the women, these average figures were not much inflated by a few very large figures. The median values were similar: £7.70 and £10.80, respectively. Four in 10 lone parents who smoked, spent more than £10 a week on cigarettes; nearly a quarter of couples spent more than £20 a week.

These figures are best interpreted as a proportion of net disposable income. This is estimated as each household's total net income from all sources, minus their housing costs (ie the amount they actually pay in rent or mortgage repayments). This is important because so many low income families have all or most of their housing costs met directly from benefits.

The lone parents and couples who smoked, spent the same average of 10 per cent of their net disposable household income on cigarettes. Table 4.2 looks at the distribution of this proportion among the three main target groups among the sample of low income families. Very few of the moderate income families spent more than 10 per cent of their disposable income on cigarettes, nor did the lone parents in work and getting family credit. More of the family credit couples did so, 4 out of 10 spent more than 10 per cent on cigarettes. But the group drawing most attention were the out of work families: half of them spent more than 10 per cent and a quarter of the out of work couples spent more than 20 per cent, recording an average of 12 per cent.

Table 4.2 Proportion of net household income spent on cigarettes by out of work, family credit, and moderate income families.

	Out of work %	Family Credit %	Moderate income %
1 – 5 per cent	21	35	51
6 – 10 per cent	30	36	39
11 – 20 per cent	25	17	9
21 – 30 per cent	23	11	6
Over 30 per cent	2	2	*
	100	100	100
Average	12%	9%	7%
Median	10%	7%	5%

Most of these out of work families were receiving income support. Looking solely at the out of work families on income support, it is possible to compare the amounts spent on cigarettes with the weekly amounts received in income support for the adults in the family. In

1991, in the case of lone parents this was £39.65; for couples, £62.25. They received additional payments for their family and lone parent status, and an amount for each child ranging from about £13 a week for the youngest up to £24 for the eldest.

On average, lone parents who smoked and who relied solely on income support, spent 21 per cent of the adult component of their income support on cigarettes. We can suppose that in only relatively few cases was this cost abated by hand rolling their own cigarettes. In the case of couples, this figure was a little higher: 24 per cent. It is worth remembering at this point that 56 per cent of lone parents on income support smoked, but 73 per cent of couples on income support had one or other or both of them smoking cigarettes regularly.

Broadly speaking, then, half of lone parents and three quarters of couples on income support spend typically a fifth of the adult part of their income support on cigarettes. Among lone parents, the range of this statistic is quite tightly bunched around an average of a fifth: between a low of 10 per cent and a high of 40 per cent. Among couples it was more widely spread because of the greater variation introduced by the difference between single and dual smoking couples. As a result, among couples on income support who smoked, 4 out of 10 spent more than 25 per cent of the adult component on cigarettes; more than 1 in 10 of them spent more than 40 per cent.

These figures have some interesting implications. It is possible to characterise tobacco taxation, representing at the time of the survey 76 per cent of the retail price, on average, as a kind of claw-back mechanism for social security benefits paid to low income families with children. It recovers almost 17 per cent of the income support paid for the maintenance of adults to such families who smoke. Since such families are the majority, this amounts to a recovery of 10 per cent of *all* adult income support paid to families with dependent children. This added up to about £530 million in 1991. This means that about 7 per cent of the total revenues raised from tobacco taxes (£7.8 billion) were raised from families with dependent children who lived on income support. Figures such as these put tension into the policy aim of suppressing smoking though taxation.

Is this a fair point? It is possible to characterise any indirect tax as a means of recovering any benefits or concessionary transfer from government: VAT and mortgage tax relief, for example. Under the present tax and benefit regime, it is a perfectly valid position to be paying income tax and claiming means tested social security benefits at the same time. A lot of family credit recipients do this. It becomes a valid comparison when the coincidence of tax and benefit bear most on a disadvantaged sector of the population. The coincidence of a volume of payment of tobacco tax that is double the national average, found among the lowest income families who rely on social security benefits for all of their income, seems to be a rare but acute example of such a valid comparison.

We must now address the most difficult part of the analysis: what difference does it make? Does the payment of tobacco tax on this scale among low income families really make a difference to the relative well being of the families who pay it compared to similar families who do not buy cigarettes?

Welfare
Well-being among low income families
It was one of the key objectives of the research programme to collect considerable detail on standards of living. A wide variety of questions were asked, which attempted to measure each of a number of different facets of well-being. Some of the indicators were based on objective circumstances, such as whether the family had a car or a television set available to them, being able to afford essential items of food, clothing and activities, problems with debts and so on. Other questions were more subjective; how well or badly did families feel they were managing on their money?

The impact of smoking
Money that is spent on cigarettes represents a use of income that is then unavailable for other purchases. In families where income is tight, other things being equal, spending money on cigarettes may be expected to reduce spending on 'necessities', and therefore to have a marked effect on overall well-being.

Of course, 'other things' are rarely equal. Proving that additional smoking has a deleterious impact on welfare is far from straightforward. Low welfare is known to be associated with lone parenthood, benefit dependency, and living in rented accommodation. Yet, as the previous chapter showed clearly, these are all factors associated with an increased prevalence of cigarette smoking.

It is, as a consequence, simple to show that smokers have a worse time of it than non-smokers. But then, we know that smoking is concentrated in the worse-off households. The more difficult question that may be put is whether, and the extent to which, smoking introduces a new source of hardship – over and above those already experienced by badly off families in the same or similar circumstances.

It is probably worth reminding ourselves that welfare cannot be simply 'read off' from people, nor indeed from survey data. Instead, it has to be inferred from a wide range of information on specific areas of life. The effect of smoking may impact rather differently upon different areas of well-being. Smoking may, for example, have a severe impact on current spending, and hence on purchases of food, but show little importance for a family's stock of durable goods which is based on longer term circumstances.

Hardship experienced by children is often paid special attention, since it is perceived as more undesirable than poverty among childless adults. Therefore it is particularly important to analyse the welfare of children as separate from that of adults. Or, at least to question whether smoking has a greater effect on the one rather than the other.

Material hardship
Within the report based on the original data (Marsh & McKay, 1993), hardship was defined as the sum of the following indicators.

- *Social participation*: not being able to afford each of a list of 30 'essential' items of expenditure and consumer durables, especially basic kinds of food, clothes, social activities and household items.
- *Debt*, especially 'problem debts' whose interest or minimum payment schedules cannot be met.
- *Financial anxiety*: feeling that the family really cannot manage and is in deep financial trouble
- *Spontaneous judgements that other items of needed expenditure were foregone*, both for adults and for children.

These are all well-established measure, that have been widely used in studies of this kind. It is less common for a single study to collect details in each of these areas.

Detailed analysis showed that a measure which incorporated all of these elements varied with income, and with the demands placed on family resources. Families on family credit were somewhat better off than those on income support, especially among the lone parents. In turn, the moderate income families, whose incomes placed them up to 25 per cent above the level which would have ended their entitlement to family credit, were better off than the family credit families. We encountered a mystery in that the eligible non-claimants of family credit seemed better off than the claimants, despite having lower incomes. But this appears to have something to do with the greater numbers of owner-occupiers among them, indicating that their better welfare scores were associated with higher incomes in the past. It is always important to remember that welfare is a product of income and resources over a period of time.

The survey also included a few of the best-off lone parents. Few lone parents have a sufficient combination of earnings and maintenance to place them beyond the scope of means-tested social security benefits. Among those few who did have such incomes, almost none experienced hardship of the kind measures by the questionnaire.

We propose to take two approaches to establish the connections between income, smoking and hardship. First to look directly at the most important indicators of hardship individually and see the extent of differences between smoking and non smoking low income families. If there is little difference, there is anyway no case to answer. If there are large differences we then have to control for the effects of income and social circumstances to determine the independent contribution made by smoking to difference in family welfare. For this we will use the summary measure.

Smoking and welfare
Social participation
Peter Townsend (1979), and others (eg Mack & Lansley, 1985) have popularised the notion that poverty may be defined as 'an enforced lack of socially perceived necessities' (Mack & Lansley, 1985; page 39). The definition of what is to count as a necessity is made clear:

It aims to identify a minimum acceptable way of life not by reference to the views of 'experts', nor by reference to observed patterns of expenditure or observed living standards, but by reference to *the views of society as a whole*. This is, in essence, a *consensual* approach to defining minimum standards. (page 42, italics in original)

In this study, a range of questions derived from this type of research were asked. They may usefully be divided into those which relate to items of food spending, those relating to clothing or leisure items, and questions on consumer durables. It could be argued that the first of these, food, would be the most sensitive to current income, whereas the last would be affected more by income in the medium or long term. Let us then look most closely at smokers' and non-smokers' ability to provide a basic diet.

For each item, respondents were asked whether they had it. Where the good or service was absent, respondents were asked the follow-up question: 'Do you not have ... because you don't want it or because you cannot afford it at the moment?'. This was to identify those families who did without various goods through choice – whether someone fails to eat meat every other day must be interpreted very differently in vegetarian as opposed to low income meat-eating households[1]. The items used were the ability to afford a hot meal every day, meat or fish every other day, roast meat joint (or its equivalent) once a week, fresh vegetables, fresh fruit, cakes and biscuits on most days.

The approach we took was to count up the number of items that were foregone owing to lack of money. It is a little arbitrary where a cut-off may be made between one level of hardship and another. The comparisons between smokers and non-smokers are, however, little affected by the precise choice of the relevant threshold. Table 4.3 illustrates the relationship between smoking status and the number of food items foregone due to lack of money. The questionnaire contained 6 such items.

A majority of each group were able to afford all the six items of food consumption. If they did without, it was usually through choice. Nevertheless, smoking had an important impact. Among lone parents, 69 per cent of non-smokers were able to afford (or chose to do without) all six items. This was true of barely a majority among lone parents who smoked. Among lone parents who spent nothing on cigarettes, 18 per cent said they could not afford 2 or more 'essential' food items, but 31 per cent of the smokers said this.

Among couples, on this most basic measure of welfare, there is a fairly clear gradient by smoking status. Where both adults smoke, welfare

---

[1] As with most of the welfare questions, the respondent was almost invariably the mother within couples. There is evidence that food, and other household resources, may be shared inequitably between the partners in couples (see Charles & Kerr, 1985), but we did not attempt to investigate this form of inequality.

is at its lowest. Moreover, this group were rather worse off than in households where even just one adult smoked, whilst the best off households were those containing no smokers. In households where just one partner smoked, having the male adult as the smoker tended to harm welfare more than if it was the mother who smoked. In household were both adults smoked, 26 per cent said they could not afford 2 or more items of food 'essentials'; in households where no-one smoked, 9 per cent said this.

Table 4.3: number of food items currently unaffordable

Column percentages								
	Lone parents			Couples				
	All	Smokers	Non-smokers	All	Both	Father	Mother	None
Cumulative number of food items foregone								
	%	%	%	%	%	%	%	%
None	59	51	69	71	58	67	73	77
1 or more	41	49	31	29	42	33	27	23
	100%							
2 or more	25	31	18	15	26	18	16	9
3 or more	14	17	11	8	12	8	9	4
4 or more	5	10	5	3	5	5	1	1
5 or 6	3	3	1	1	2	2	–	–
6	*	1	–	*	1	–	–	4
	100%							

Information relating to 'social participation' was also available for consumer durables, and for the purchase of items of clothing and of leisure services. There is no need to repeat the detailed examination of this information, because the broad pattern was the same as that presented above. Among lone parents, smokers tended to go without to a greater extent than among non-smokers. Couples where both adults smoked were unambiguously the worst off, and couples with no smokers the best-off group. Families containing just one smoker were in an intermediate position, but there was no evidence that families were systematically worse off if the father rather than the mother was the smoker.

Item by item, having a smoker in the family almost doubled the chances of reporting a lack of some essential item; having two smokers in the family increased these chances between 2 and 3 times. For example, 14 per cent of non-smoking couples said they could not afford 3 or more of the 9 clothing and leisure items compared with 36 per cent of the dual-smoking couples.

The welfare of adults and children

In the section above, we showed that smokers tended to have lower levels of welfare than non-smokers, as measured by being unable to afford items that most people would take for granted. This was true whether we considered food spending, consumer durables, or articles of clothing and for leisure. Special attention was given to the food items because adults will find it the most difficult to exclude their children from its effects. This in many ways is the most important question we address in this report. It is possible to say that free choosing adults have a perfect right to go without nourishment in order to be able to smoke. In Hilary Graham's studies some of even the poorest mothers defended their habit as a means of avoiding weight gains. The defence of individual choice does not deny the need to continue to urge, educate or use other means to encourage people to give up. Nor does it deny the argument put forward in the previous chapter that the great excess of smoking among low income families is caused by their poor circumstances and not a special love of the freedom to smoke. But if it were be shown that parents' smoking was directly affecting the welfare of children, then a new dimension, and a new urgency, would enter the question of what might be done about it.

We extracted 5 questions that seemed more closely related to the welfare of children than to that of adults: the inability to afford for each child, two pairs of all-weather shoes, a weatherproof coat, a best outfit, toys and sports gear, and spontaneously saying that there were other things needed for children that parents '... just can't find the money for.' This provided a measure of child well-being, as captured by 5 questions on social participation, and of adult well-being, based on 22 items.

Simple tabular analysis showed that the smokers did less well on each measure. The greater the number of smokers within the household, the greater the average number of items that could not be afforded. There were few differences between welfare as measured for adults, and that measured for children.

Table 4.4 shows the details of the child-based 5-item scale. Among lone parents, the proportion saying that they could not afford 2 or more of the five items rose from 25 per cent among non-smokers to 44 per cent among smokers. Among couples, 17 per cent of non-smoking couples said they could not afford 2 or more items. This figure rose sharply to 30 per cent among families where the mother alone smoked and to 35 and 36 per cent where the father alone or both parents smoked.

The average figures given in Table 4.5 show clearly the magnitude of differences in welfare between smoking and non-smoking households for both the adult and child items. Broadly, smoking is associated with a one and a half-fold increase in the average number of items foregone for both adults and children when either a lone parent of one parent of a couple smokes, and a twofold increase when both smoke.

Table 4.4 number of child items currently unaffordable

Column percentages

		Lone parents				Couples		
	All	Smokers	Non-smokers	All	Both	Father	Mother	None
Cumulative number of child items foregone								
None	41	39	49	54	42	49	49	66
1 or more	59	61	51	46	58	51	51	34
	100							
2 or more	36	44	26	27	36	35	30	17
3 or more	22	29	13	15	23	14	18	9
4 or more	10	12	7	5	8	3	5	4
All 5	2	3	2	2	3	3	1	1

Table 4.5 Mean items currently unaffordable

		Lone parents				Couples		
	All	Smokers	Non-smokers	All	Both	Father	Mother	None
for adults	5.3	6.1	4.4	3.4	4.8	3.8	3.3	2.5
for children	1.3	1.5	1.0	0.9	1.3	1.1	1.1	.7

The nature of this conclusion is clearly central to this research. While a multivariate analysis will be presented below, it is important to see just how robust is this relationship between smoking and child welfare, when income status is controlled for. We are, of course, looking at a sample of low income families and differences in income have already been kept to a minimum. Even so, some of these measures may show a particular sensitivity to small changes in income.

A simple method of keeping income fairly constant is to consider just those families receiving certain (means-tested) benefits and compare them with those receiving none – the moderate income families. In the sample, there are large numbers of family credit recipients, and quite large numbers of lone parents receiving income support. By making comparisons for just these groups, we may have a greater insight into whether the above relationships are an effect of smoking, or merely tell us that smokers are disproportionately represented amongst the most poor groups (Table 4.6).

Table 4.6 Mean number of items currently unaffordable

| | Lone parents | | | Couples | | | | |
	All	Smokers	Non-smokers	All	Both	Father	Mother	None
Moderate income families								
for adults	2.3	2.9	2.0	1.9	2.7	1.9	2.1	1.6
for children	.8	.8	.8	.5	.7	.5	.5	.3
Family credit recipients								
for adults	4.4	4.9	3.8	4.7	5.2	5.1	4.8	4.2
for children	1.0	1.2	.8	1.3	1.4	1.3	1.5	1.1
Income support recipients								
for adults	6.1	6.7	5.3	5.9	7.4	<– 5.7 –>		3.7
for children	1.5	1.7	1.2	1.5	1.9	<– 1.5 –>		.9

Table 4.6 contains a great deal of information, but may be summarised relatively simply. For each family type, recipients of family credit did rather better than those on income support but rather worse than the moderate income families. This reflects the differences in the final incomes of each type of family.

Among lone parents, smokers and their children did worse than non-smokers in each case, except among the moderate income families. If a lone parent has even moderate income, her smoking does not much affect her children's welfare but on FC or IS, it does.

Among couples, smoking was associated with a rise in the average number of both child and adult items foregone among each type of family. The differences in the child items were least among the family credit families but greatest among the income support families, for whom the average doubled from one to two. This may not seem very much, but it means, for example, that the proportion saying that they could not afford 2 or more child items rose from a only a fifth among non smoking couples on income support, to a half of those where either or both parents smoked.

There is another way of looking at Table 4.6. About half of the considerable differences in the adult social participation aspects of welfare seen between the benefit and non benefit families was accounted for by smoking. All of the differences between the family credit and income support families were accounted for by smoking. A child of a non-smoking family out of work and on income support was actually *better* off than a child of a smoking family in work and receiving family credit and only a little worse off than a child of a smoking family among the moderate income group.

Subjective assessments of well-being
A direct approach to determining families' standard of living is simply to ask them. Families could be questioned on how they assess their financial management, or just, more generally, how well off they feel. With this type of information, more than other types, the wording that is used to generate the data will be crucial. It is often difficult to escape a kind of bland, uniform response that the family is doing 'all right', that things could (of course) be better, but that doubtless many others are worse off.

Among this sample of low income families, however, there was little reticence about families expressing disappointment about their financial situation. We asked two questions, that had the following wording:

a) *How often, would you say, have you been worried about money during the last few weeks?*
… almost all the time/quite often/only sometimes/never
b) *Taking everything together, which of the phrases on this care best describes how you and your family are managing financially these days?*
… manage very well/manage quite well/get by all right/don't manage very well/have some financial difficulties/we are in deep financial trouble

These are fairly standard questions. In most surveys there would a noticeable clustering of responses around the middle responses -people tend to think that they 'get by' in a fairly average way, and few admit to either severe difficulties or to managing very well either. This sample, composed only of low income families, was rather different. No less than 42 per cent of the sample admitted to worrying about money almost all the time (possibly, all the time). A further fifth said they worried about money 'quite often'.

Needless to say, the presence of smokers was associated with a rather greater frequency of monetary concerns. 55 per cent of lone parents who smoked worried about money almost all the time, compared to 43 per cent of the non-smokers. Among couples where both partners were smokers, 46 per cent were perpetually concerned about money, falling to 30 per cent of couples where neither smoked.

The second question, on financial management, had a similarly pessimistic set of replies. Four per cent said they were in deep financial trouble. Remarkably, the figure was almost one in ten (9 per cent) of those lone parents who were smokers. Nearly one fifth (19 per cent) of low income families agreed with the rather euphemistic statement that they had 'some financial difficulties'. Among couples where both smoked, this accounted for 24 per cent of families: it was only 17 per cent of the non-smoking couples.

Among the relatively few families (4 per cent overall) who said both that they were in deep trouble and managed badly, three quarters of the couples and 6 out of 7 of the lone parents smoked.

The number and size of any debts
Finally, in this analysis of the individual constituents of well-being, we consider the importance of debt. Recent research by the PSI (Berthoud & Kempson 1992) indicates that debt is generally associated with low income, or with large commitments relative to income.

A large proportion of this sample – 39 per cent – reported that they had one or more debts that were proving difficult to repay. Almost one fifth overall (19 per cent) reported two or more such debts. Smoking was closely related to the incidence of debt: 27 per cent of lone parents who smoked had two or more debts, compared to 14 per cent of the non-smokers. Among couples, the incidence of having two or more debts was one-quarter where both adults smoked, but little more than one in ten (11 per cent) where neither smoked.

Constructing a composite measure of well-being

Each of the sections above outlined the relationship between smoking status, and various pieces of information on family welfare. In almost all cases, smokers were worse off than non-smokers. Couples were particularly likely to face poor circumstances if both adults smoked. Previous research by the authors (Marsh & McKay 1993) has indicated that each of the measures outlined is linked to income in predictable and reliable ways, and to the various commitments of various households. Moreover each of the components of well-being tend to be associated with one another – enough to indicate that they are measuring broadly the same underlying concept, but not to such an extent that they cover the same information.

There are a number of ways in which an overall measure may be constructed. We must select which data are to contribute to the measure, and decide which of them are to be regarded as more important than others. However, it is usually best to opt for a simple approach unless there are good reasons to depart from the straightforward. We took the view that each of seven areas of material well-being should be included.

A 7-point index (lowest = 0, highest = 6) of relative financial and material hardship was constructed, adding one point for each 'yes' answer to the following questions:

Does the family have … ?

1. Two or more problem *debts*?
2. Two or more items on the *food* list scored 'unable to afford'?
3. Three or more items on the *clothing and leisure* lists scored 'unable to afford'?
4. Four or more items on the *consumer durables* list scored 'unable to afford'?
5. *Both* the financial anxiety measures scored at the highest point ('Always worried about money' *and* 'In deep financial trouble')?
6. *Both* the questions asking for *spontaneous estimates of items need* for adults and children named by respondent?

This scale ignores community charge arrears; does not count, in some cases, up to six items of basic expenditure scored 'unable to afford', ignores those who worry constantly about money unless they (only 4 per cent overall) also say they are in real trouble, and disregards the lack of any savings. This means that to get any kind of score on this scale means to experience some hardship. Such difficulties are not that uncommon among low income families, so the scale was designed to pinpoint severe hardship.

The analysis of these data in the main body of work undertaken in this programme of work on low income families showed a clear break-point in the welfare index. Families could just about cope with one or even two of these composite markers for hardship. But families scoring three or more on this scale, 20 per cent of the sample as a whole, were, relative to other low income families (to say the least of it), in severe hardship. It was therefore decided to use this point on the scale as the cut-off point that distinguished 'severe hardship' from more common-place levels of financial stress.

Analysis revealed a clear distinction between the relative disadvantage of the families receiving means-tested benefits (income iupport and Family Credit) and the relative advantage of those on relatively modest incomes, but not receiving these benefits.

The strong correlation between smoking and hardship was, of course, repeated when the overall welfare index was analysed (Table 4.7)

Table 4.7 Proportion in severe hardship

Lone parents	27%
Smokers	33%
Non-smokers	19%
Couples	14%
Both smoke	27%
Father smokes	17%
Mother smokes	11%
Neither smoke	6%
Total	20%

Among lone parents, a third of smokers met our definition of severe hardship – scoring 3 or more on the index – compared with a fifth of the non-smokers. Compared to all lone parents, only half as many couples were in severe hardship (14 per cent versus 27 per cent) but the gradient of hardship associated with smoking was even steeper. Only 6 per cent of non smoking couples were in severe hardship. When the mother alone smoked, this figure all but doubled, when the father alone smoked, it all but tripled, when both smoked it increased four and a half times to 27 per cent. Put simply, smoking couples are as badly off as the average lone parent.

Earlier analysis indicated that the relationship between welfare and various socio-economic circumstances followed the same contours as that established for smoking in the previous chapter: the full details are reported in Marsh & McKay (1993). Welfare tended to be higher when families were not receiving means-tested benefits, and when they had no recent experience of receiving such benefits. Housing tenure proved to be extremely important. Social tenants were the group facing the greatest material stress; owner occupiers appeared to be faring best. Smaller families were more likely to avoid financial difficulties than families with more children.

Towards a multivariate analysis of welfare
This section presents one of the central dilemmas of this report, which may be summed up in the following three points.

- An earlier section established that low income families were more likely to smoke if they were on benefits, had fewer qualifications, were in manual employment, rented rather than owned their homes, and so on.
- This chapter has set out the ways in which smokers appear to have much lower standards of living than non-smokers.
- Previous research by the authors has shown that low welfare is more likely for tenants, and for those on benefits, among other effects.

In other words, we do not know whether smoking has a negative impact on standards of living, *independently* of the fact that smokers are drawn from those families who face the worst constraints and perhaps have the fewest opportunities.

This suggests that the detailed analysis that remains will need to deal with a more detailed question. Do smokers have a lower standard of living than non-smokers, controlling for all other factors? This question calls for more sophisticated techniques than have been deployed in this chapter to date and, as in the previous chapter, we turned to the use of logistic regression but this time predicted whether or not families were in severe hardship.

The effect of smoking on hardship

We begin with a summary of the key results. Among lone parents, controlling for other known factors, smokers are more likely to be found in severe hardship than non-smokers; among low income couples with children, smokers were affected in a similarly adverse way but the effect on hardship was most severe, and clearly so, when both adults were smokers and when disadvantage was greatest (Table 4.8).

There was considerable experimentation with the variables entered into the equations. It was shown in the last chapter that the background factors that predict smoking did so at least partly independently of one another. This is not true of the relationship between these same background factors and hardship, despite the close relationship between hardship and smoking. For example, the use of 'manual work' as a background factor became problematic, especially among lone parents. Manual workers were worse off than non-manual workers and they were more likely to smoke, true enough. But manual workers in or recently in work were better off than those who had had no job at all in the recent past and who were even more likely to smoke. Afro-caribbean and, especially , Asian families had the lowest rates of smoking, some of the lowest incomes but they had some of the lowest hardship scores too, but this was only true among couples. Marital status is also overtaken by other variables in the analysis. Single and separated lone parents, for example, are more likely to be in hardship because they are income support claimants and social tenants.

For clarity and simplicity it proved most sensible to run summary equations using the most important variables found in the previous chapter as background predictors of smoking itself and eliminate those that did not, independently, predict hardship too. These remaining variables were: being white, receiving income support, receiving family credit, being unqualified and being a social tenant. The results of these calculations can then be presented most simply by extracting the most important factors and estimating by how much they increase or decrease the likelihood of hardship, independently of other significant factors, relative to the same reference person, or couple, used in the equations in the previous chapter.

Whereas the equations shown earlier to predict smoking were complex, adding up to a powerful combined explanation of the relationship between all aspects of social and economic disadvantage and increased smoking, this analysis turned out simpler. Any two or three aspects of disadvantage will provide a good estimate of whether or not a family is in hardship. The important point is that, whatever aspects are used, smoking increases that estimate significantly, independently of other factors. The most disadvantaged families who do not smoke are still significantly less likely to be in hardship that the most disadvantaged families who do.

Thus, if you want to guess whether a lone parent is significantly more likely than another lone parent to be in severe hardship, you really need to know need to know only two things: is she on income support, and does she smoke? Knowing she is unqualified and white helps you more, but not much more. To make the same guess about low income couples, you need to know three things: are they on income support, are they social tenants, and do they *both* smoke? Knowing they are cohabiting helps more, but not much more. Nothing much else will improve your guess, except that if you take out social tenancy from the analysis, a lack of educational qualifications substitutes almost as well. The same is true among lone parents. We believe this is a very important point that will be taken up in the next chapter.

These measures clearly tap the key independent features of the power of economic and social disadvantage to predict both smoking and poverty at the same addresses. The probabilities shown in Table 4.8 are, of course, just probabilities estimated from a model, and models are not perfect. They illustrate the importance and independence of different factors upon hardship. But it would be an advantage to show something of the actual scale of differences as they occur in the data.

We therefore constructed a very simple index of social disadvantage. Each of the markers for disadvantage found earlier to be independently associated with smoking were coded '0' or '1' (absent or present): social tenancy, no qualifications, claiming income support, doing manual work, being never married (or cohabiting). (The scale for couples has more values because they get two chances to be unqualified or a manual worker.) Families who have none of these disadvantages, even lone parents, seldom experienced severe hardship. Indeed, almost the only families among these least disadvantaged families who experienced any hardship were the relatively few smokers among them. (Table 4.9)

Table 4.8 Logistic Regression analysis predicting hardship

Lone Parents	Reference person is non-smoker, she is a low income white lone parent who is a tenant, receiving income support, has some educational qualifications and did non-manual work when employed, and she is divorced.

	Probability of being in severe hardship
Not on income support	12%
On family credit, not IS	17%
Owner occupier	29%
Reference lone parent	**34%**
Single, never married	39%
Smoker	51%

Couples	Reference couple are not 'dual smokers' (one or other might smoke, but not both), they are also white, tenants, do non-manual work when they can but are now on income support, they are married and one of them has some educational qualifications.

	Probability of being in severe hardship
Owner occupiers	10%
On family credit, not IS	21%
Reference couple	**23%**
Wife does manual work	27%
Neither has any qualifications	32%
Both smoke	38%

Table 4.9 Smoking, hardship and disadvantage: proportion in severe hardship

	cell percentages					
	Lone parents		Couples			
	Smoker	Non-smoker	Both	Father	Mother	None
Index of disadvantage						
None	10	2				
One	24	8	12	0	0	2
Two	29	17	17	7	15	5
Three	33	26	23	15	10	11
Four	40	26	35	28	19	12
Five or six			40	27	17	14

As the markers accumulated, so hardship became more common, rising to a third of the most disadvantaged lone parents and a quarter of the most disadvantaged couples in severe hardship. But this rise was far steeper among smokers than it was among non-smokers. These are the most important features of this relationship.

- *Among non-smoking families, the rise of hardship with increasing disadvantage was shallower.* Among lone parents, who we know are anyway prone to hardship, it rose from almost zero to about a quarter of the most disadvantaged but non-smoking lone parents. Among non-smoking couples, the rise was even shallower: still no more than 1 in 7 of the most disadvantaged non-smoking couples were in severe hardship.

- *Among couples, having one smoker in the household raised the likelihood of severe hardship only a little.* To this extent the increase in hardship associated with mother or father smoking (Table 4.7) is accounted for by greater disadvantage among smokers sooner than by smoking alone. The effects of fathers' smoking was the greater but it had its significant impact only at the worst levels of disadvantage.

- *Among all-smoker households, the rise of hardship with disadvantage was very steep.* What was particularly striking was that the rise was identically steep among couples and lone parents: one in ten of the least disadvantaged smoking families were in severe hardship. As disadvantage accumulated, the proportion in severe hardship rose to a quarter, to a third, and finally to four out of ten among those having more or less the full set of disadvantages that composed the scale.

- *'Dual-smoking' among couples erased the difference in welfare between couples and lone parents.* It was said earlier that smoking made the average dual-smoker couple as badly off as the average lone parent. Controlling for levels of disadvantage in this way (since lone parents are so much more disadvantaged and badly off compared even to low income couples) shows us that dual-smoking couples are as badly off as smoking lone parents.

- *The impact of smoking on the rise of hardship among smokers is redoubled by earlier evidence that smokers are twice as common among the most disadvantaged.* The most important conclusion of the last chapter was that disadvantage doubles smoking. The most important conclusion of this chapter is that, independently of disadvantage, smoking doubles hardship. Among the less advantaged half of couples, dual smoking triples hardship.

5   Summary and Conclusions

This study examined the incidence of smoking among Britain's low income families. It revealed a growing dilemma in smoking control policy: the increasingly regressive effects of tobacco taxation upon increasingly larger numbers of poor families, especially those with dependent children.

The problem

Over the past two decades, the prevalence of smoking has declined among higher income groups. Among the lowest income quarter, it has not declined at all. This has left an increasing proportion of smokers among the poorest families. At the same time, an increase in income inequalities, particularly among families, combined with a rapid growth in lone parenthood, has created a closer and closer association between smoking and family poverty in general, and between smoking and women's poverty in particular.

These trends have continued at an increasing pace, resulting in a doubling of the numbers of children in poverty, most of them in families relying on means-tested social security benefits for most or all of their income. They, rather than other children, are those most likely to share their homes with parents who smoke.

This problem has been made more urgent by an increased reliance on price policy as the first and most important means of controlling smoking. Britain does not quite have a 'one club' smoking control policy, but the emphasis on price has been strengthened, partly in response to evidence of its overall effectiveness, partly to resist the continental European trend towards advertising bans. The tax on tobacco products will continue to be raised so as to increase the retail price at a rate currently more than twice that of overall price inflation. Tobacco taxation remains an important source of government revenue, approaching £8 billion a year.

The suspicion has grown, on the other hand, that the burden of tobacco taxation has fallen hardest on those least able to bear it. That the policy is least effective among the poorest smokers who have dependent children. The policy dilemma that has been created is a complex one. The thesis of this study, building on previous work by Graham and others, is that the disadvantage, inequality and hardship experienced by low income parents causes them to be much more likely to smoke compared with other, better off families.

This likelihood is raised not by a perverse desire among the poorest to take up smoking despite their slim means. Three quarters of all income groups take up smoking when they are young. It is caused by the difficulty they have in giving up.

They cleave to the anodyne qualities of tobacco and defend their habit on grounds of entitlement in disadvantage and of solidarity with others in the same circumstances. But the cost of smoking deepens their hardship. They are caught, we proposed, in a malign spiral: most likely to take up smoking; least able to give up smoking; least able to afford smoking; most likely to suffer material hardship; and most likely to suffer increased hardship because of their expenditure on cigarettes. What was the evidence?

The families

Evidence was sought first in a re-analysis of families both with and without dependent children interviewed the General Household Survey and, in more detail, from the DSS/PSI survey of low income families. The latter survey interviewed 2,200 of Britain's low income families with dependent children whose household income left them less than 25 per cent above their entitlement threshold for family credit. This sample covered the lowest quarter of the relative family income distribution. It also included 900 lone parents, two thirds of whom lived on income support. Generally speaking, low income families defined in this way either had benefit incomes, or had earnings less than half the national average.

Chapter 2 provided a summary of the characteristics of Britain's low income families. There was a clearly observable 'fault line' running through the population of low income families that placed the two kinds of 'benefit family' (those in work and claiming family credit, or out of work and claiming income support) on one side and the non-benefit families (eligible non-claimants of family credit and the moderate income families) on the other.

Compared to the non-benefit families, the benefit families, tended to be the lone parents, except the widows. Among couples, they tended to marry less and cohabit more. They tend to be younger and to have more children. They were less well educated and had fewer qualifications. They were more often found in unskilled jobs. More than anything, though, they tended to be social tenants rather than owner occupiers, usually in council housing.

Smoking among low income families

The new analysis of the 1990 General Household Survey, using income rather than social class to stratify families, showed clearly the extent of concentration of smokers among the lowest income quarter. This was true of families with and without children (up to age 44) except that lone parents were much more likely to smoke compared with single women of similar age and income who had no children. The size of these differences was large. The least well off families were more than twice as likely to smoke compared with the better off.

This is a recent phenomenon. Re-analysis of the 1986, 1980, and 1976 General Household Surveys showed that reductions in smoking prevalence have been confined to higher income groups. For example, in the 1980s married men and women in the highest income quarter halved their smoking. In the lowest income quarter, 6 out of 10 of the lone parents smoked in 1976, 6 out of 10 in 1990; half the couples smoked in 1976, half in 1990.

The DSS/PSI survey of low income families was then used to unpack further differences in smoking behaviour *within* each significant group of low income family. For example, the GHS had shown that 6 out of 10 lone parents smoked, but prevalence in the DSS/PSI survey was lowest among widows, highest among single and separated lone mothers, and among lone fathers. Overall, though, being a lone parent significantly raised the likelihood of smoking, independently of other factors. Similarly, among couples, those cohabiting were far more likely to smoke than those married. An important additional factor among couples was the association between husbands'. and wives' smoking. Smokers marry smokers.

The most striking differences were associated with housing tenure. Social tenants, the majority among low income families, were twice as likely to smoke compared with owner occupiers.

This was especially true of those living in flats: 4 out of 10 children of flat-dwelling families lived with *two* adult smokers. This has implications for their health, as well as their material welfare.

Much higher smoking rates were also associated with lower status manual work (especially cleaning and catering) among those in work, with receipt of income support among those not in work (especially among married men), and with having no educational qualifications.

Multivariate analysis indicated that, quite surprisingly, all these factors, all these markers for disadvantage, acted to raise the prevalence of smoking independently of each other. Lone parenthood, marital or former marital status, housing tenure, manual work, poor education, receipt of means tested social security benefits, all made an independent and significant contribution to raising the likelihood that a low income parent would smoke.

Their combined effects were impressive. For example, among lone parents who shared even two of these markers for disadvantage (social tenants in manual work, for example) 7 out of 10 smoked. And among unqualified couples who were social tenants and income support claimants, 7 out of 10 of the husbands smoked and, getting on for half of them reported both husband and wife smoking cigarettes regularly.

There was one striking exception to this tendency. Whereas minority ethnic status is usually held to be an additional marker for disadvantage, far fewer Afro-Caribbean lone mothers, very few Asian men, and almost none of the Asian women smoked.

It cannot be stressed too strongly that these results were observed *within a sample of low income families*. It is possible, therefore, to look more optimistically at these figures and note that even among low income families, those who have remained a married couple, who got into low cost owner occupation, who achieved even modest educational qualifications, who have albeit lower paid non-manual work, and who have managed to avoid contact with the Department of Social Security, are really no more likely to smoke than anyone else. This evidence suggests that it does not take very much in the way of social and economic improvement to inoculate the majority of men and women against smoking. It is when one disadvantage combines with another, and then another, that low income families smoke in so much greater numbers. Put most simply: disadvantage doubles smoking.

Evidence from the National Child Development Study confirmed these results for a large sample of 33 year olds, of all income levels, with and without children. On the other hand, giving up smoking was associated with improving financial circumstances. The power of social milieu in these results was also demonstrated by the residually high levels of smoking among those who had bought their council homes, compared with other owner occupiers.

Above all, NCDS showed for the whole range of incomes, how important is the coincidence of social tenancy and a lack of educational qualifications in raising smoking prevalence, and how three quarters of all income groups take up smoking and half give up before their early thirties; except the poorest smokers who do not give up.

What appears to have happened is that the concentration of unqualified school-leavers in the council estates of the 1970s became a protected social habitat for high levels of smoking not seen elsewhere since the early 1960s. Whatever has happened in the mainstream of British society, in what a senior cleric called 'comfortable Britain', that has caused so many to turn aside from smoking, it has passed these people by. Interviewed in 1991, they had become Britain's lowest income families, many of them lone parents. And they were still smoking.

Hilary Graham observed that '… smoking is acquiring a new social profile, as a habit it follows the contours of social disadvantage'. It does. Even among the restricted range of disadvantage within Britain's low income families, it marks every peak, traces every valley. You can almost study social disadvantage itself through variations in smoking prevalence.

The effects of smoking

Evidence from the Family Expenditure Survey for 1991 showed clearly that low income families with children spent at least twice as much on tobacco products compared with high income families. These differences were of exactly the same magnitude as those suggested for prevalence by the GHS and by our own survey, and this suggested in turn that the costs of smoking for low income families were not much abated by use of hand-rolling tobacco. This is anyway unlikely because so many of our low income parents were women, few of whom roll their own cigarettes, and hand-rolling in Britain now accounts for a tiny proportion of the market.

Overall, lone parents and married mothers who smoked, smoked exactly the same average of 15.6 cigarettes a day; married fathers smoked 17.4. The average cost per smoking household was about £8.60 a week for lone parents, £14.10 for couples. Among families whose total incomes were, respectively, £86 and £144 a week, this represents a considerable expenditure: 10 per cent of net disposable income.

Among families on income support, the majority of whom smoked, it represented a very considerable expenditure. Among couples on income support, 73 per cent bought cigarettes at a cost of about £16 a week. This represented 15 per cent of their net disposable income. It was, on average, a quarter of the adult component of their income support. This means that nearly half of couples who smoked spent more than a quarter of their adult income support on cigarettes. Among lone parents who were on income support and who smoked (who were more than a third of *all* lone parents) the gross cost was lower (£9.20 a week) but the net proportions of income and income support were the same.

More and more, tobacco taxation has become a device that claws back social security benefits. For example, tobacco tax recovers for the Treasury nearly 17 per cent of all income support paid for the support of claimants who are parents of dependent children and who smoke. This recovery amounted in 1991 to £530 million a year. Seven per cent of all tobacco revenues are taken from parents on income support.

The impact of this expenditure upon families relative material welfare was considerable. To measure welfare we used a wide range of indicators, including items of normally essential expenditure foregone, problem debts, anxiety about money, and so on. Difficulties of these kinds were common among our sample of low income families. But, on each indicator, on average, smoking families were twice as likely to say that they experienced each kind of material and financial difficulty compared with non-smoking families. Hardship increased sharply as smoking increased. This was especially true among couples and worst among couples on income support.

These effects impacted directly on children as well as upon adults in families who smoked. Whereas many low income parents will say that they themselves go without in order to be able to buy cigarettes, they will suggest that they try to protect their expenditure on their children from the effects of their buying cigarettes. The evidence suggests that in many cases they do not succeed. For example, couples on income support who both smoked were more than twice as likely to say that they lacked food, shoes, coats, and other necessary items *for their children* compared with couples on income support who spent nothing on cigarettes.

This wide ranging information on different aspects of material well being was combined into a single measure of hardship, defining a fifth of all low income families as experiencing *severe* hardship. Among lone parents, a third of the smokers were in severe hardship compared with a fifth of the non-smokers, though clearly, smoking is not the sole cause of hardship among lone parents. But it worsens what are, on average, already difficult circumstances for many.

Among couples, the differences were larger. More than a quarter of the dual-smoker couples were in severe hardship, falling to 6 per cent of non-smoking couples. Among couples, then, a mother alone smoking almost doubled the likelihood of severe hardship (11 per cent), a father smoking almost trebled it (17 per cent), both smoking raised it four and a half times (27 per cent).

The most important question for the analysis was to determine the extent to which the greater hardship experienced by smokers was caused by their smoking or by their greater disadvantage compared with non-smokers. The disadvantages that apparently increase the chances of smoking also, of themselves, increase the chances of hardship. Did smoking increase hardship independently of marital status, low income, manual work, lack of education, social tenancy, claiming benefits, and all the other things that cause some families to be poorer than other families?

It did, and to a quite striking extent. Multi-variate analysis confirmed what the earlier analysis had suggested. Independently of other factors, smoking was associated with higher levels of financial and material hardship among low income families at each level of income and in each position of relative advantage and disadvantage. The greater the extent of disadvantage, and the lower the income, the harsher was the impact of tobacco expenditure on hardship. This impact fell equally on adults and children.

It is important to stress that smoking was not the sole cause of hardship among low income families. Most of them have these difficulties of one kind or another and even severe hardship was by no means confined to smokers. It was an additional cause of hardship, one quite the equal of, say, having no qualifications or being a social tenant. It accounted for about half the shortfall in family welfare observed between the benefit families and the 'moderate income' families just above eligibility for benefits. The most important point of all was that, even among a sample of families sharing the lowest quarter of family incomes, smoking caused hardship most among the most disadvantaged low income families.

Conclusions

Supporters of the use of taxation to reduce consumption of tobacco have won the attention of policy makers. Cross-nationally, they point to evidence that suggests a reliable coefficient: each 1 per cent increase in real price will be followed by a 0.38 per cent fall in consumption. Townsend suggests for Britain alone a better ratio of 1 per cent to 0.5 per cent. This is at the margins, of course. No-one suggests that a 200 per cent increase will eliminate all smoking overnight. And the relationship between price increase and prevalence – a more important issue than consumption – is a rather more elusive figure. But a steady incremental approach is accepted by most policy-makers. Townsend estimates that a phased increase in the real price of 55 per cent per cent will, together with other measures, save 31 per cent of all projected deaths from lung cancer and 46 per cent of all smoking related deaths by 2019, let alone all the other havoc visited upon the nation's health by cigarettes.

These are impressive figures and it is not surprising that governments are responding. It is easy to put up the price of cigarettes, within reason. Governments always like to be seen to be 'doing something' about a national health problem and they have no objection to a course that also increases short term tax revenues. France, for example, increased tobacco taxation by 30 per cent in two stages, in January and May 1993. In November 1993, the British Chancellor of the Exchequer increased the price of cigarettes a further 5 per cent and promised future increases annually 3 per cent above inflation.

But the evidence of this study seems clear: if the purpose of tobacco taxation is to stop smoking most effectively among those who really cannot afford to smoke and who have most to gain by giving up, this policy is not working. Those least able to afford cigarettes are those most likely to smoke. Worse, almost the *only* people who genuinely cannot afford to smoke: the very lowest income families supporting young children, are at least twice as likely to smoke compared even to similar families who could only just afford to smoke if they wanted to.

Unlike most people, the lowest income families really do have other strong reasons for wanting to smoke. They alone in our society are under the greatest pressure, experience the greatest inequality of choice and opportunity in their lives. Some of them, especially the lone parents, feel they exist solely to service their children's daily needs. They have to do so at a level so basic, it removes them entirely from the 'real' world of people who have comfortable homes, cars and holidays. To repeat Hilary Graham's telling phrase culled from many encounters with women in these circumstances: smoking is their only luxury. They defend it, aggressively sometimes. In a world of many luxuries for others, one luxury for oneself becomes a necessity.

If the policy is not working with poor smokers, a new policy is needed. One of the discouraging aspects of the prospects for a new policy is that all the parties with an interest in this area have been looking the other way. Those with an active interest in family welfare seem never to discuss it. Researchers overlook the issue. For example, University of York recently published recent work on the adequacy of social security benefits for the support of families (Bradshaw, 1993). They calculated a 'modest but adequate' family budget and contrasted its composition with a 'low cost budget'. Smoking was explicitly excluded from both, yet our own study has shown that the inclusion criterion – that about two thirds should purchase an item deemed by them essential – is clearly met for benefit families in the case of cigarettes. And they spend 15 per cent of their disposable income on cigarettes. It is quite urgent to start new research to show in more detail exactly what this does to the rest of their expenditure, for themselves and for their children.

Politicians and policy makers hardly ever discuss the issue, and the policy of increasing tobacco taxation is pressed ahead without any discussion of its effects on low income families. An interesting question to ask of policy makers is: supposing *only* the poor smoked? If present trends continue, the question will become more and more realistic. For example, people bringing up young children in council accommodation are only about 4 per cent of the whole population, but they are getting on for 1 in 10 of all smokers. (Remember too that there are many more poor smokers who have no children.) What then? A policy towards tobacco control would become, indivisibly, a policy towards poverty. Given the position of policy towards supporting the incomes of families with children, there would have to be an explicit linkage between tobacco control policy and the priority of child welfare. We suggest that once such a policy linkage is made, as increasingly it should be made, increasing tobacco taxation above inflation might be almost the last thing anyone would think of.

What indications for policy are provided by this study?

The very high levels of smoking among low income families is first of all, a response to poverty. Its expense deepens their poverty and effectively blocks their way out. This malign spiral, it seems to us, is caused by the discouragement borne of disadvantage and inequality. All modern research on how people give up smoking shows that people do so for reasons connected to optimism. They will get more of what they want in terms of self esteem, self-presentation, and so on; they will get less of what they fear, in terms of ill health; and they expect to achieve this without being reduced to a nervous wreck, they say.

Britain's lowest income parents are not people with great cause for optimism, or for self-esteem. Coping with their children on benefit incomes raises so many short term difficulties they obscure any long term considerations like the longer healthier life non-smoking might offer. In contrast, those low income families who have only a little more reason for optimism, who have only a little better quality of life, turn out to be no more likely to smoke than most other people who are substantially better off.

This at least is ground for policy optimism. It is impressive how small a rise in the quality of material life is associated with a sharply lowered incidence of smoking.

In contrast, those families who do not participate in any of this raised quality of life are the families among whom smoking doubles, and more. This excess of smoking prevalence *must* be connected in some way to their material circumstances, to their poor life chances, and, more than anything, we suspect, to the kinds of pressure exerted by being a parent of young children and not having enough resources, of all kinds, to provide the kind of quality of life most people think a reasonable minimum for them.

It is of course possible to argue, and we expect some will try, that the relationship is not causal, that both the hardship experienced by low income families and their smoking arise from some deeper factor within them. These may be unintelligence, low self-esteem, personal incompetence, or sheer fecklessness that causes them to be both enduringly poor and to smoke.

The superficial attraction of such explanations tends to overlook some difficult corollaries. Still the majority of smokers are not poor. Nor are they stupid, cast down or feckless. They may be behaving foolishly toward their health in this aspect but they compete well enough with non-smokers in other areas. Millions of better educated, efficacious, well-off people smoke, and do so for their own reasons, not just because they can afford it. It cannot be right to have one explanation for smoking among the poor and another for everyone else.

This is not to deny that personal characteristics play an important role. Smokers are quite likely to be responding to anxiety, or depression, lack of optimism or self esteem, and many other kinds of negative affect they feel. It is similarly right to argue that such feelings are more commonly found among the poorest families with small children, most commonly found among lone parents, for example. But it makes far more sense to hold that such feelings arise from their difficult circumstances, not the other way round. The discouragement they feel about their lives and their futures simply raises the probability that the easiest, locally approved, legal anodyne for anxiety will be taken up: cigarette smoking.

Yet, an unsympathetic reaction to these findings might be to suggest that, if low income families waste their money on smoking, then social security benefits could and should be lowered. But the strongest evidence of this study is that increased hardship would cause a rise, not a fall in smoking among this population. This is objectively what happens already.

A policy that lowered benefit levels for the large minority of income support families who do not smoke, solely on the ground that the majority do, would strain everyone's sense of equity.

And a policy that tried to reduce the benefits of poor smokers alone would be doomed to farce. Though, of course, we have shown that this effectively is what tobacco taxation does already.

If, as we have said, smoking, or rather a greatly increased incidence of smoking among poor families, is a response to poverty, it follows that the way forward out of this policy dilemma will be one that links smoking control policy to family welfare policy. For example, if the present policy continues, and greater and greater revenue is raised from Britain's remaining smokers, some thought might be given to mobilising this additional money in family health and welfare support. If it cannot be returned in cash, for other considerations of work incentives and so on, then it seems reasonable to argue that a small fraction of the tobacco tax yield, a fraction far smaller that the one poor smokers themselves contribute, could be mobilised in community health interventions.

The foregoing is but a hypothetical example of what such a policy linkage between smoking control and family welfare might mean. There must be others. It is important to remember that these people did not start families, place themselves on a low income, and then irresponsibly decide to take up smoking. They took up smoking as children, as many people did. Their circumstances have since prevented them from giving up, as many people did. There must be a case for a whole package of measures to assist low income families to overcome the special difficulties they have in giving up smoking. Making aids like nicotine gum and patches available on prescription would deliver them free to families on income support and family credit, for example.

But main purpose of this report was to make plain some uncomfortable facts and to start a debate, not to prescribe a remedy. It *is* a very hard dilemma to confront and it is not all that surprising that the problem has evaded open policy review. But it is a problem that is growing more urgent; cigarettes are already 7 per cent more expensive in real terms than they were when our families were interviewed. Further real increases in tobacco price will cause further real decreases in the material welfare of poor families who smoke, including reductions in the material welfare of their children. This will affect the majority of poor families. Those who smoke most, the very poorest families, will be affected the worst.

Despite this apparently negative conclusion, it is possible to see these results in the light of opportunity. This study has clearly identified the main target if Britain is to meet its declared aim of reducing smoking prevalence to 20 per cent by the year 2000. Britain's poor families are the last heartland of normative smoking. Only here are people still *expected* to smoke. Yet the smaller numbers among them with more cause for optimism – the better qualified non-manual workers buying their homes – have already followed the national trend away from smoking.

If sufficient of the huge tax yield poor smokers themselves contribute can be mobilised into a new assault on the problem, then an important opportunity arises. The resources could be ploughed back into a serious multi-level effort to break the hold that smoking has in poor communities, on a previously untried scale. If it succeeds, then the whole national problem of smoking will be well on its way to resolution. Once smokers are a clear minority among this last host community for the habit, the trend will do the rest, just as it is doing among the better off. Once smoking has gone, it will not come back. One of the worst pandemics in the story of our national health will be over.

References

ASH Working Group on Women and Smoking (1993) *Her Share of Misfortune* Action on Smoking and Health,

Charles and Kerr (1985) *Attitudes to the Feeding and Nutrition of Young Children*, Health Education Council, London.

Berthoud R & E Kempson (1992) *Credit and Debt*: The PSI Report London: PSI

Bradshaw J. and J Millar (1991) *Lone Parent Families in the United Kingdom* London: HMSO

Bradshaw, J. (1993) *Household Budgets and Living Standards* Joseph Rowntree Foundation, York

Fry, V and P Pashardes (1988) *Changing patterns of smoking: are there economic causes?* London: IFS, Report Series No. 30

Godfrey, C (1988) "Licensing and the demand for alcohol" *Applied Economics,* 20, pp 1541–1588

Graham, H. (1988) Women and Smoking in the United Kingdom: the implications for health promotion, *Health Promotion*; 4: 371–382

Graham H. (1992) *Smoking Among Working Class Mothers with Children*, Unpublished Report, Department of Health

Haskey, J.(1993) Trends in the numbers of one-parent families in Great Britain. *Population Trends*, No 71, Spring, London: HMSO

Jones, G. (1988) *Smoking Behaviour Among Mothers*, Unpublished report, London, Thomas Coram Research Unit

Lader,D. and J. Matheson (1991) *Smoking Among Secondary School Children in 1990* OPCS, HMSO, London

Lewit, E and D Coate (1982) "The potential for using excise taxes to reduce smoking" *Journal of Health Economics*, 1, pp 121–145

Mack, J & S Lansley (1985) *Poor Britain* London: George Allen and Unwin

Madely, R.J., P. Gillies, F.L. Power and E.N. Symonds (1989) Nottingham Mothers Stop Smoking Project – baseline survey of Women in Pregnancy, *Community Medicine* 11, 2: 124–30

Marsh A. and Jil Matheson (1983) *Smoking Attitudes and Behaviour* London, Her Majesty's Stationary Office

Marsh A. and Joy Dobbs (1983) *Smoking Among Secondary School Children*, London, Her Majesty's Stationery Office

Marsh, A (1984) "Smoking: Habit or Choice?" *Population Trends* No 37, Autumn, pp. 14–20.

Marsh, A (1985) "Smoking and Illness: What Smokers Really Believe" *Health Trends* No 1, Vol 17, February, pp. 7–13.

Marsh, A & S McKay (1993) *Families, Work and Benefits* London: PSI

McKay, S. and A. Marsh (1994) *Lone Parents and Work: the effect of benefits and maintenance*, Research Report No. 25, Department of Social Security, HMSO, London.

Millar J (1989) *Poverty and the Lone Parent Family* Aldershot: Avebury

Office of Population Censuses and Surveys (1991) *General Household Survey: Cigarette Smoking 1972 to 1990*, OPCS Smoking Monitor, 26th. November, ss 91/3

Office of Population Censuses and Surveys (1991) *Family Spending in 1991*, HMSO, London.

Office of Population Censuses and Surveys (1978) *Family Expenditure Survey, 1976*, HMSO, London.

Pahl, J. (1984) 'The allocation of money within the household'

in M. Freeman (ed.) *The State, the Law and the Family* Tavistock, London.

Popay G & S Jones (1991) "Patterns of health and illness among lone-parent families" in M Hardey & G Crow (eds) *Lone Parenthood* London: Harvester Wheatsheaf

Schelling, T (1986) "Economics and cigarettes" *Preventive Medicine,* 15, pp 549–560

Simms, M. and C. Smith *Teenage Mothers and their Partners*, Research Report, London, Her Majesty's Stationary Office

Sutton, S, A. Marsh and Jil Matheson (1987) "Explaining Smoker's Decision to Stop, Test of an Expectancy-value Approach" *Social Behaviour* Vol 2, 1987, pp. 35–49.

Thomas, M., E. Goddard, M. Hickman and P. Hunter (1994) 1992 *General Household Survey*, OPCS, HMSO, London.

Townsend, J (1987) "Cigarette tax, economic welfare and social class patterns of smoking" *Applied Economics,* 19, pp 355–365

Townsend J. (1988) Price, Tax and Smoking in Europe, in: Patti White, ed. *Tobacco Price and the Smoking Epidemic,* Copenhagen, World Health Organisation

Townsend, P (1979) *Poverty in the United Kingdom* Harmondsworth: Penguin.

Wald, N. et al (1988) *UK Smoking Statistics* Oxford University Press